SCIENCE BETWEEN SPACE AND COUNTERSPACE

Author's Final Errata

Page 31 line 4, replace μ_2^2 with μ^2

Page 37 line 8, replace τ with π

Page 64 bottom line, replace first ϕ with Φ

Page 95 third line from bottom, replace n_2 with n^2

Page 114, delete { in line labelled (1)

Page 140 line 18, replace $\phi=0$ with $\phi=90°$

Page 143 line 9, replace $b=$ with $\beta=$

Page 154 line 5, replace $\sqrt{b-A}$ with $\sqrt{B-A}$

Page 154 equation (7), move $-\sqrt{A}$ to end of equation

Page 156 line 8, insert "between the plane" after "the angle"

Page 167 equation (4), insert denominator $8A_4^2(A_1+A_2+A_3)$

Page 170 equation (1), replace $\sqrt{x^2+x^2}$ with $\sqrt{x^2+z^2}$

Page 173 line 8, replace $cos(\theta/r)$ with $cos(\theta)/r$

SCIENCE BETWEEN SPACE AND COUNTERSPACE

Exploring the significance of negative space

Nick Thomas

NEW SCIENCE
London

New Science Books
Temple Lodge Publishing
51 Queen Caroline Street
London W6 9QL

Published by New Science Books 1999
(New Science Books is a division of Temple Lodge Publishing)

A catalogue record for this book is available from the British Library

ISBN 0 902636 02 3

Cover by Studio MAOSS, incorporating a geometric design by Nick Thomas
Typeset by DP Photosetting, Aylesbury, Bucks
Printed and bound in Great Britain by Cromwell Press Limited, Trowbridge, Wiltshire

CONTENTS

ACKNOWLEDGEMENTS

I would like to thank:

My wife Heather whose moral support was invaluable

The Anthroposophical Society in Great Britain for sponsoring the work

Alec Schaerer who made a generous donation for the cost of publication

Many friends, especially in Scandinavia, who encouraged me

The Science Section of the School of Spiritual Science for encouragement and for getting the book started

Jim Kotz for his valuable help in checking the manuscript

New Science for having the courage to publish it, and Eileen Lloyd for her editing.

INTRODUCTION

This book describes the exploration of an idea by the author. The consequences proved to be more far-reaching than expected and the enterprise is very far from complete. It is shared here largely because of requests to make it available rather than because it is in any way finished. It is a description of where the author has arrived at the time of writing, and it is expected that things will have developed further by the time it appears. It must thus be seen as a provisional statement at best.

The aim of the work is to show that science may benefit from the inclusion of the holistic aspects of another kind of space, and to seek an understanding of the many research findings of Rudolf Steiner in relation to a scientific view of the world so that a spiritual understanding may be shown to be fruitful. This is not meant as an apology for a dogmatic standpoint, and indeed some of its features may be seen by others as in conflict with Steiner. The author has not started from Steiner's findings and tried to justify them, but rather has taken certain ideas seriously and followed their consequences, which has then thrown light on them. Steiner's books and lectures are viewed here as research reports of considerable interest and far-reaching consequence, but research reports are just that—statements of the findings of a researcher which deserve careful study and checking. It is the author's conviction that these reports are worth serious scientific study as they point to radically different ways of thinking about the world which developments in science certainly seem to call for (e.g. Refs 6 and 25).

Steiner reported that in a higher state of consciousness a different kind of space is experienced that is polar opposite to our ordinary Euclidean one. Such a consciousness looks in from the periphery towards an unreachable inwardness in contrast to our normal consciousness which looks out from a centre towards an unreachable outwardness, i.e. towards an outer infinity. When describing his research on the sun he said that however bizarre it may sound, the space of the sun is negative. This has come to be referred to as *counterspace*. George Adams found a way of describing this space mathematically, formally as a polar-Euclidean space with a different kind of metric basis from ordinary space. His ideas are presented amongst others in Refs 1, 2, 3 and 4, apart from a large collection of unpublished notes. Louis Locher-Ernst arrived independently at similar ideas (Ref. 22).

Steiner indicated that the use of projective geometry provides a very good starting-point to study his findings as it entails wholeness and is free of the standard metric of our usual approach to ordinary space. Hence it is used in this book as a starting-point although much more is required besides. The author sought a way of taking the ideas of Steiner and Adams further in this respect, and had the idea that if counterspace is an actual component of reality then objects may be related to both spaces at once (generally other workers have assumed this only for living organisms). The kernal of the idea is more than that, though, and involves the notion that *strain* arises due to the different laws of the two spaces which may be in conflict for a *linked* object. That in turn may be answered by a *stress* which then leads to action. The terms strain and stress are used technically as in engineering, as explained later. When different geometries between projective and metric geometry are considered, linkages appropriate to gases and liquids become apparent and their duals in relation to counterspace suggest states of ether which Steiner also described. This opens the way to a study of the strains and stresses appropriate to the states of matter and also in relation to light, chemistry, life and heat. A new theory of gravity arises and some well-known experimental results in the realm of gases and optics are derived.

The book is an exploration of this overall proposal, and initially the intention is to see if it can explain known phenomena in a different way as a check on its viability. That should open the way to new predictions which can be tested, but resources should not be expended until the whole picture is sufficiently in focus to warrant that. The field is vast and the work of one person in relation to that of countless gifted workers in the field of science this century must seem inadequate, but the possibilities that have opened up seem worth sharing. An overall consistency has been striven for but as yet is incomplete, so what is being shared is 'work in progress' rather than a polished product.

Science uses models and the question of the truth lying behind them is interesting, although some philosophers have eschewed the issue of truth. Sir Karl Popper sought truth, Paul Feyerabend despised it and Thomas Kuhn appears neutral. The author is interested in the truth and finds, like Einstein and Bohm before him, the Copenhagen Interpretation of quantum physics unsatisfying. Truth must lead where it will, not where we want it to. A model is a kind of analogy which clearly shares some concepts with the truth or it would not work. So we will not be surprised to find formal similarities with existing models, and indeed we hope for that; but a different underpinning for those models arises.

The mathematical level is what is needed to present the work rather than an introductory one, apart from a brief introduction to projective geometry (although some technicalities have been relegated to appendices). It is not intended as a pedagogical textbook but a research report. The chapter on chemistry reflects a cutting edge of the work and requires fairly advanced mathematics for its exposition, and no attempt has been made to simplify it. The chapter on life represents a rather tentative beginning which is included for the sake of completeness. It does begin to show how other areas may come together in a coherent whole.

Broadly speaking the order of presentation is that of the route taken by the author, and the whole enterprise is iterative in nature as advances in one area reflect back on others—and that process is still under way.

The following symbols and abbreviations will be used throughout:

O   The CS infinitude
Ω The plane at infinity in space
wrt with respect to

1. PROJECTIVE GEOMETRY

The investigations presented in this book are based on projective geometry. The main reason for this is that it underlies all other geometries based on linearity, and provides an inherent approach to holistic questions as it entails the principle of duality. Although there are many excellent works on the subject, e.g. Refs 8, 9, 10, 27, 40 and 42, we will give a very brief introduction as the subject has become unfashionable, and then in subsequent chapters revert to more advanced methods. We cannot justify everything in detail, as this is not a geometry textbook, so the reader is invited to consult the references for more information.

The subject arose from a study of perspective, and was instrumental in leading geometry away from its metric heritage to the study of relationships and incidence without reference to angles, lengths, areas and volumes. We see this illustrated in Fig. 1.

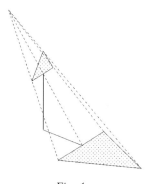

Fig. 1

If we think of this as a light throwing a shadow of a signpost we note that none of the angles, lengths, or areas are the same in the shadow as in the original. However incidences and straightness are preserved, assuming the road is flat. It is an example of a *transformation* which systematically converts one figure into another. Projective geometry essentially involves all those transformations which are *linear*, which in this case takes straight lines into straight lines and planes into planes, and of course points into points. However linear transformations can also be *polarities* which take points into planes and vice versa, and lines into lines, as shown in Fig. 2.

Two points are shown on the right as vertices of two cones tangential to a sphere. The two shaded planes are determined by the circles of

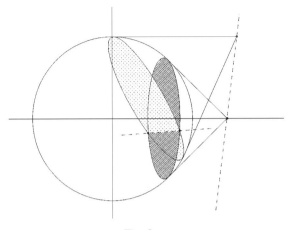

Fig. 2

contact of those cones. In this way all points in space outside the sphere may be related one-to-one to planes intersecting it. It is essential that such a transformation is reversible if it is to be linear. And clearly this is true here as if we started with the two planes we would find the circles in which they cut the sphere; construct the tangent cones at those circles and hence find the same points corresponding to the planes as the vertices of those cones. Notice that the original two points determine a line (shown dotted) that corresponds to the line of intersection of the planes (also shown dotted). In fact the construction may be extended to points inside the sphere also, so that with a little extra work a unique plane can be found corresponding to any such point. More generally, transformations that preserve the type of elements, taking points into points and planes into planes, are called *collineations*, while transformations such as the polarity above that swap the roles of points and planes are referred to as *correlations*.

It should be clear from the above examples that if a point lies on a line then the transformation of that point will lie on the transformed line, and similarly if a line lies in a plane their transforms will be incident, as is the case if a point lies in a plane. If two lines intersect then so will their transforms. These kinds of relation are called *incidences* and an essential feature of projective geometry is that incidences are preserved by its transformations.

Thus linear transformations preserve incidences, straightness, flatness (of planes) and are reversibly one-to-one. There is only one number that is unchanged or invariant, known as the *cross-ratio*. It is a ratio of ratios and is illustrated in Fig. 3.

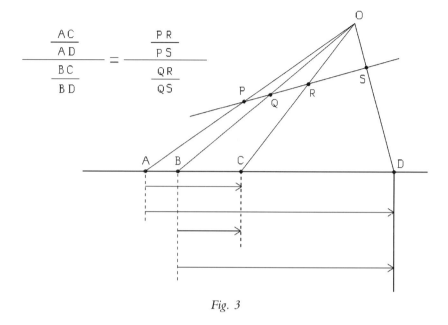

Fig. 3

The four points ABCD determine the four lengths AC, AD, BC and BD which taken in the double ratio shown give an invariant, and for the transformed range PQRS the double-ratio formed in the same way for corresponding points gives the same result. The process of *projection* of a range from a point such as O above and *section* by a line such as PQRS are typical projective processes, and may be repeated starting from PQRS to give a third range and so on. No matter how many times this is repeated the cross-ratio of the final range will equal that of ABCD. What is even more interesting is that if we start with a different initial centre in place of O and go through a different series of projections and sections such that three corresponding points of the final range coincide with those reached through the first series, then the two fourth points also coincide. Thus if the first sequence leads to the range A'B'C'D' corresponding respectively to ABCD, and the second series transforms ABC into A'B'C' then its fourth point will also be D'. This is the *fundamental theorem* of projective geometry. Thus we can speak of *the* transformation of ABCD into A'B'C'D' since the result does not depend upon the route taken. The same applies to corre-lations. A linear transformation that preserves cross-ratio is often called a *homography*. There are peculiar forms of projective geometry that do not preserve cross-ratio, but we will not be concerned with them. The lines in the point O are said to form a *flat pencil* which also has a cross-ratio, which is most easily found from that of the range on a line intersecting it.

We say that any two lines meet in one and only one point, which implies that parallel lines also meet in a point. This is not true in Euclidean geometry, but in projective geometry so-called *ideal* points are added to Euclidean space to 'close' it. Two parallel lines are said to meet in an ideal point and two parallel planes in an ideal line. The sum total of ideal points and lines make up the ideal plane at infinity. Finally this plane is regarded as after all being ordinary and it is only our consciousness that makes it seem special. To illustrate this the following transformation (Fig. 4) shows how the ideal line in a plane may be transformed into an ordinary line.

The transformation is a special projective transformation known as a *homology* where corresponding points such as A and A′ lie on a line through the *centre* O and corresponding lines such as AC and A′C′ intersect on a fixed line s called the *axis*. One pair of corresponding points must be given, which we will suppose are A and A′. We will now transform the parallel lines AQ and CP meeting in an ideal point we will call I, and also AB,CD meeting in another ideal point we will call J. The transform of AQ must contain A′ and Q. To transform CP we note that AC and A′C′ must meet on s and CC′ contains O, which fixes C′. Then the transform of CP is C′P. A′Q and C′P meet in the point I′ which is thus the transform of the ideal point I. Similarly AB and CD transform into A′B′ and C′D′ meeting in the

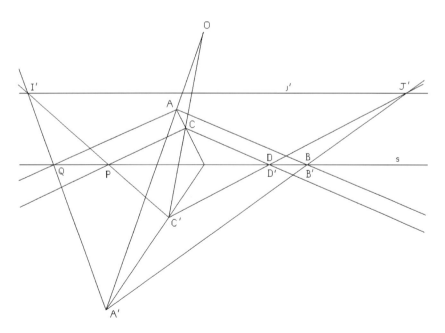

Fig. 4

point J'. The points I' and J' determine the line j' which is the so-called
vanishing line because it is the transform of the ideal line at infinity. If the
process is repeated for other pairs of parallel lines it will be found that their
transforms always meet on j', a fact which is proved in elementary texts.
Thus by a projective transformation we have transformed the ideal line into
an ordinary one, which demonstrates that all the ideal points in the plane
lie on a line since lines are always transformed into lines, and also that
infinity is not an invariant for projective geometry. Similarly the ideal
points in space can be shown to lie on a plane. Strictly speaking 'infinity' is
not a projective concept since it is not an invariant for this geometry, which
then implies that the ideal points are, for it, ordinary points; they are only
'ideal' from a Euclidean perspective.

The duality inherent in projective geometry is what is important for us,
which was discovered by Poncelet and developed by Gergonne and Jakob
Steiner. An example in the plane is that any two distinct points determine a
unique line, and dually any two lines determine a unique point. An
interesting historical example lies in two theorems that were discovered
independently and then found to be duals of each other and thus really
amounted to only one. Pascal discovered the theorem illustrated in Fig. 5
on the left, and Brianchon discovered that on the right. These theorems are
for plane geometry where points and lines are dual. On the left we have six
points $AB_1CA_1BC_1$ on the conic forming a hexagon. The opposite sides

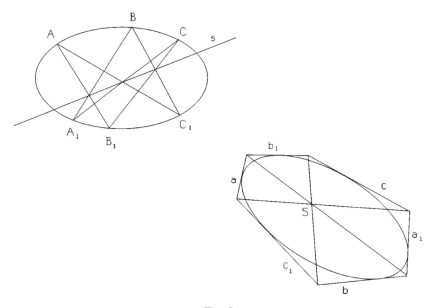

Fig. 5

AB_1 and A_1B meet in a point. There are three such cross-joins of opposite sides and the theorem states that the three resulting meeting-points always lie on a line (s). Pascal established this for all conics when he was 17 years old. On the right we see an ellipse with a circumscribed hexagon, and the lines joining opposite vertices meet in a point S. Brianchon proved that those three lines are always concurrent for any conic whatever. However these two theorems are dual since if for Pascal's Theorem we replace all points by lines and all lines by points we obtain Brianchon's configuration, as the lettering is intended to show where lines are labelled by lower case letters corresponding to the dual labelling of the points on the left. The conic is self-dual in a special way: it is regarded on the left as a locus of points but on the right as an envelope of lines.

In three dimensions every theorem also has its dual where points and planes exchange roles, lines are self-dual and surfaces as loci are dual to surfaces as envelopes of tangent planes. The concept of counterspace to be introduced in the next chapter requires a careful application of this principle.

The important feature of ideal points is that they *function* in the same way as ordinary points, e.g. in transformations, which enables us to treat them as equals in projective geometry. A further extension of the geometry is possible where more subtle entities also function as points although they are even less accessible to the imagination. They are the so-called *imaginary* points, which we will introduce through the concept of the *projective measure*.

Figure 6 shows a transformation of the line p into itself. We set up the transformation by arbitrarily selecting two centres of projection P and Q,

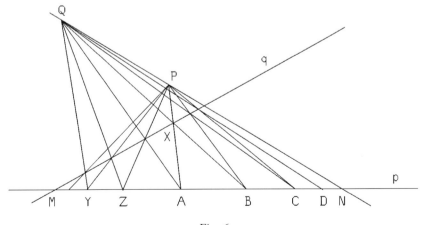

Fig. 6

and a line q. Starting with a point A on p we join it to P and then find the point X where P meets q. We then join Q to X, giving a line which meets p in the point B. Thus the transformation, which is projective since it only involves projections and sections, transforms the point A into B. We then start with B and transform it into C, and so on. We can also go backwards from A to give Z,Y etc. The resulting set of points is said to form a *measure*, but the essence of the measure lies in its behaviour. It will be seen that the sequence approaches but never reaches the point N on the right, and for the reverse sequence M is likewise never reached on the left. The two points M,N are self-corresponding, and an important theorem states that there are at most two self-corresponding points, for should there be a third then all points would be self-corresponding and the measure would be lost. This measure is referred to formally as a *hyperbolic* measure, or after Adams a *growth* measure. The transformation finds for every point on p a corresponding point, for it can also be applied to points outside the segment MN, and illustrates the important idea that a line can be transformed into itself such that its points move in a characteristic manner, noting that our starting-point A could be chosen anywhere other than at M or N.

If we choose P, Q and q such that the line PQ intersects q on p then M and N coincide, giving a *parabolic* or *step* measure. It is also possible to set up a measure with no self-corresponding points, which is illustrated in Fig. 7 where we show on the left an equivalent way of constructing a growth measure using a circle, and then use that on the right to construct an *elliptic* or *circling* measure.

On the left the two lines q and PQ have been replaced by a circle, noting that a line pair is a special form of conic section, and the measure on p is

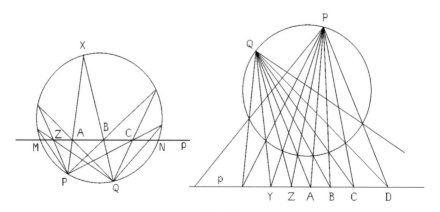

Fig. 7

shown. The previous method of construction can be set up to produce this measure and it will be found to give identical results. The double points M, N are where p meets the circle. On the right p is taken outside the circle and a measure is produced with no double points. However if the quadratic equation is set up to find the points of intersection of p with the circle, it has real roots on the left and complex conjugate ones on the right. In some sense there *are* two double points on the right which are said to be *imaginary*. They function like points and von Staudt developed a method of approach which requires no algebra, which is explained in detail in Ref. 10. There can also be imaginary planes, and in space there are two types of imaginary line.

This extension of projective geometry to include imaginary elements is important when we come to relate it to metric geometry as we will see in the next chapter.

2. SPACE AND COUNTERSPACE

Rudolf Steiner experienced a different kind of space which forms an essential part of the world. It is polar opposite to our ordinary space and has variously been referred to as negative space, polar Euclidean space and counterspace. We shall use the latter term. This space has an inward infinity instead of an outer one and the explorations in this book concern the way it may relate to ordinary space, to make a start towards accounting for our scientific observations in a non-materialistic way. George Adams, a colleague of Steiner's, found a way of characterizing it mathematically, which has been presented in Refs 1, 2, 3 and 4 amongst others. We will now examine how this is done starting from projective geometry, and we will use the analytic method for the sake of brevity. The rigorous underpinning of this, assumed without comment below, is to be found in Refs such as 27 and 38. We will now assume the reader is familiar with projective geometry and the analytic approach to it.

We distinguish space from geometry, the former being an aspect of the world we experience while the latter is pure mathematics. Euclid's exposition concerned *metric* geometry, related to the word itself which means measurement of the earth. Measurement assumes that certain standards are invariant, so that a ruler or protractor is unaltered as we move it about, a centimetre remaining the same regardless of the orientation or position of the ruler, an angle of $30°$ that of the protractor. A more modern approach treats geometry in terms of transformations and invariants, so that for Euclidean metric geometry length, area, volume and angle are invariants under the transformations characterizing it. In contrast pure projective geometry leaves none of those invariant, its invariants being linearity and cross-ratio. Its transformations are the group of linear transformations expressed by

$$\mathbf{x}' = \mathbf{P}\mathbf{x}$$

where $\mathbf{x}$ is a vector representing a point, $\mathbf{P}$ is a matrix of constants specifying the transformation, and $\mathbf{x}'$ is the new point; $\mathbf{x}$ is transformed into $\mathbf{x}'$ by $\mathbf{P}$. Homogeneous co-ordinates are used so that elements at infinity may be included, so in the plane $\mathbf{x}$ is a vector with three components representing a point and $\mathbf{P}$ is then a 3×3 matrix. Dually $\mathbf{x}$ may represent a line in the plane. If we represent a line by $\mathbf{u}$ instead of $\mathbf{x}$ then the condition for the point $\mathbf{x}$ to lie on $\mathbf{u}$ is

$$\mathbf{u}^{\mathrm{T}}\mathbf{x} = 0$$

where $^\mathbf{T}$ denotes transposition, i.e. the inner product of the two vectors is zero.

If instead we take all the lines and planes in a fixed point then $\mathbf{x}$ may represent a plane or dually a line. In this case there are no elements at infinity so it is a purer representation of two-dimensional projective geometry.

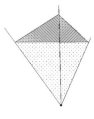

Fig. 8

In three dimensions $\mathbf{P}$ is a 4×4 matrix and $\mathbf{x}$ has four components and may represent a point or dually a plane. The transformations thus characterized are *collineations* which transform elements into other elements of the same type, so points transform into points and planes into planes. *Correlations* transform elements into their duals, so in space points transform into planes and vice versa, while lines are self-dual. The best known correlation is polarity wrt a quadric surface such as a sphere.

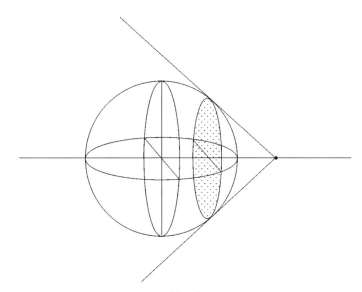

Fig. 9

In three dimensions lines are represented by Plücker co-ordinates which have six components. One degree of freedom is accounted for by the *Plücker line condition* which the six components must satisfy to represent a line, and another by the homogeneous nature of the co-ordinates, leaving four to represent the ∞^4 lines of space.

In projective geometry no element is special, and the plane at infinity may be transformed into any other plane by suitable choice of **P**. Indeed for projective geometry there *are* no elements 'at infinity', which is illustrated by the two-dimensional case above of the geometry of lines and planes in a point. It is our particular Euclidean consciousness that studies projective geometry and needs to single out a special invariant plane to accord with our experience. It was a major milestone in mathematical thought to step beyond the confines of our experience in this way and develop a geometry free of its constraints. However the *space* we live in and our consciousness of it is for normal experience Euclidean in character, and we do not expect the plane at infinity to rush in towards us when we move about! Projective geometry may be restricted by insisting that **P** must leave the plane at infinity invariant, and that points in it transform only into other points also lying in it. Then we have a subset of possible matrices {**A**} which leave the plane at infinity invariant. These transforms are called *affine transformations*, and are in fact the ones we experience visually where there is a vanishing line for perspective and lengths and angles appear to vary with our point of view. We only become conscious of the Euclidean character of our space when we move about and see that the trees in an avenue are in reality of the same height, despite the appearance that distant ones are shorter. Euclidean space is as much a thought construct as projective geometry, affine geometry lying between as a pure expression of our direct experience. Since affine transformations leave the plane at infinity Ω invariant, it follows that parallelism is conserved by them. The reason is that if two planes α, β are parallel then they intersect in a line p lying in Ω, and an affine transformation must transform p into another line p′ also in Ω, so that α′ and β′ intersect in p′ and thus are parallel. The same applies to parallel lines. Hence in a perspective drawing parallel lines all meet on a consistent set of vanishing lines. The drawing (Fig. 10) shows a set of houses illustrating this.

Thus affine geometry is very simple in concept when looked at in this way. The transformations **A** may involve expansion, contraction, rotation and translation. While lengths are not invariant, in any one direction the invariant cross-ratios may be reduced to an invariance of simple ratios known is *division ratios*. Thus if two points P_1, P_2 on a line are related to the origin O and the point at infinity I on that line, the cross-ratio (P_1P_2, OI) becomes the simple division ratio OP_1/OP_2 which is conserved by an

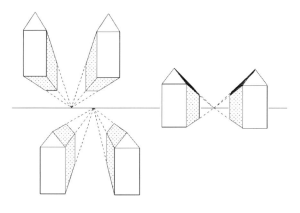

Fig. 10

affine transformation. However if Q_1 lies on a line not parallel to OI then ratios such as OP_1/OQ_1 are not invariant. Interestingly areas in the same plane may also be compared in this way (although strictly speaking area is not an affine concept), as the ratios of Euclidean areas in a plane are conserved by affine transformations. Also ratios of volumes (obviously in the same space!) are conserved. This shows the interesting fact that area and volume are independent concepts. The classification of quadric surfaces now becomes more detailed compared with projective geometry where there are three kinds of quadric: ellipsoids, ruled quadrics and imaginary quadrics.

This means for example that no projective transformation can change an ellipsoid into either a ruled quadric or an imaginary one. In affine geometry the incidence of a quadric with Ω is conserved, so if it intersects Ω in real points then so will its transform, and two-sheet hyperboloids and paraboloids may be distinguished from ellipsoids.

A further specialization is possible. If the matrix **A** has a unit determinant then the volume of a figure is absolutely invariant. Again what this means is that if the volume is found for Euclidean co-ordinates then an affine transformation leaves it invariant. Here we consider *centro-affine* geometry in which both the origin and Ω are invariant, in which case affine transformations may be represented by a 3×3 matrix which is the leading submatrix of **A**. In Euclidean language the volume of a parallelepiped (in which opposite faces are parallel) is given by the triple scalar product of the vectors representing its edges, which is the value of the determinant of the 3×3 matrix **T** with rows composed of the components of the three vectors. If we take the 3×3 matrix representation of a centro-affine transformation with determinant $|\mathbf{A}|$ then the transform $\mathbf{T}' = \mathbf{AT}$ has a

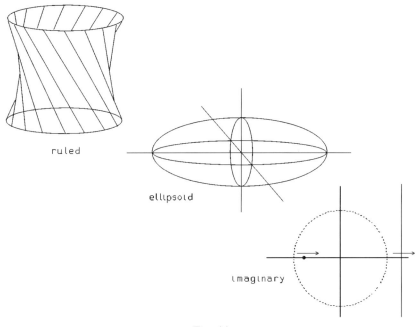

ruled

ellipsoid

imaginary

Fig. 11

determinant multiplied by $|\mathbf{A}|$ and hence a volume multiplied by $|\mathbf{A}|$. A second distinct parallelepiped $\mathbf{S}$ also has its area multiplied by $|\mathbf{A}|$, so in affine geometry the ratio of the volumes $\mathbf{T'}{:}\mathbf{S'}$ must be the same as that of $\mathbf{T}{:}\mathbf{S}$. For special affine geometry $\mathbf{T'} = \mathbf{T}$ (and $\mathbf{S'} = \mathbf{S}$) as $|\mathbf{A}| = 1$, despite the fact that the ratios of the edges of $\mathbf{T}$ will not equal those of $\mathbf{T'}$. It is noteworthy that angle is not an affine concept at all, as even ratios of angles are not conserved, and in particular the right angle is undefined.

A further specialization of projective geometry can restrict the allowed transformations to those which leave lengths and angles invariant. Cayley proposed in the nineteenth century that if a quadric surface is singled out and made invariant, i.e. only those projective transformations are allowed which leave its surface as a whole invariant, then it is possible to define length and angle in terms of cross-ratio and thus arrive finally at a fully metric geometry. His expression is

$$s = \frac{\log{(CR)}}{2i}$$

where s is distance and the cross-ratio $CR = (\mathrm{AB}, \mathrm{IJ})$ is that of the two points A, B in relation to the two points I, J in which their common line intersects the invariant quadric Q.

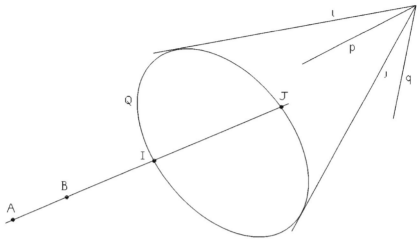

Fig. 12

A similar equation applies for angles between planes. This ensures that s is invariant for transformations that leave Q invariant as cross-ratio is conserved. The quality of the resulting geometry depends upon the quadric surface chosen. To obtain Euclidean geometry it is necessary to choose the degenerate quadric $x_0^2 + x_1^2 + x_2^2 = 0 = x_3$, i.e. an imaginary circle in the plane at infinity known as the *absolute imaginary circle at infinity*, or absolute circle for short. A plane intersects this circle in the points $(1, \pm i, 0)$ in point co-ordinates for that plane, and two orthogonal lines in it intersect their common line in points harmonically separating them. This cross-ratio will be conserved, and so orthogonality becomes an invariant. The limiting process used to evaluate the log of the cross-ratio in the case of this degenerate quadric yields the usual Euclidean sum-of-squares, but multiplied by 2i. Hence the 2i in the denominator. Ref. 12 explains this for two dimensions, and Refs 38 and 40 for three dimensions. The result for the distance between the points x_i, y_j is

$$s^2 = \frac{(x_0\,y_3 - y_0\,x_3)^2 + (x_1\,y_3 - y_1\,x_3)^2 + (x_2\,y_3 - y_2\,x_3)^2}{x_3^2\,y_3^2} \tag{1}$$

and for the angle between the two planes u_i, v_j it is

$$\cos(\theta) = \frac{u_0\,v_0 + u_1\,v_1 + u_2\,v_2}{\sqrt{(u_0^2 + u_1^2 + u_2^2)(v_0^2 + v_1^2 + v_2^2)}} \tag{2}$$

(the u_i, v_j are plane co-ordinates, which are briefly explained in Appendix 2).

In summary the steps from projective to Euclidean metric geometry are:

1. Select an invariant plane as the plane at infinity to give affine geometry
2. Restrict transformations to those with a unit determinant to give special affine geometry
3. Make the absolute circle in Ω invariant to give metric geometry

If some other quadric is chosen as the absolute then parallel lines intersect on its surface, which replaces step 1 and makes affine geometry more complicated. We emphasize these three steps for Euclidean geometry rather than Cayley's single jump from projective to metric geometry for reasons which will become clear later on.

Non-Euclidean geometries employ other quadrics as absolutes, and for example in General Relativity the metric varies from point to point in a spatial manifold. This is expressed by the metric tensor g_{ij}, which is a matrix with functions of the co-ordinates for its components (see Appendix 1 for a brief introduction to tensors and the meaning of g_{ij}). It is a symmetrical matrix and so at a definite point it may be taken to represent a definite quadric, which defines the metric at that point in Cayley's sense. However at other points the quadric may be different, which endows the space it represents with intrinsic curvature. However, real transformations such as describe an affine displacement from one point to another cannot change the type of quadric, only its shape, which is usually referred to as the 'law of inertia'. For Euclidean geometry g_{ij} is the unit matrix $\mathbf{I}$, which is independent of the co-ordinates.

Rudolf Steiner's report of a different kind of geometry led George Adams to propose that instead of selecting an imaginary circle in Ω we may choose instead an imaginary cone as the absolute, which is dual to the absolute circle. The resulting geometry is thus polar-Euclidean geometry, describing what we are calling counterspace. We will again decompose this into three steps leading from projective geometry to counterspace (which Adams did not do).

1. Select a *point* as invariant instead of a plane, giving polar affine geometry
2. Restrict the transformations to those with a unit determinant to give polar special affine geometry
3. Make the absolute cone with equation $u_0{}^2 + u_1{}^2 + u_2{}^2 = 0 = u_3$ invariant, where the u_i are plane co-ordinates. This cone has its vertex in the invariant point as $u_3 = 0$, and is imaginary as its tangent planes are imaginary.

If we followed the customary path in tensor analysis we would enquire into the way the metric defines distance between points, and we could use Cayley's formula for the cross-ratio to do so. Mathematically there is nothing wrong with such a procedure. However, if we are consistent in our dualizing then—as George Adams pointed out—we could instead define the *separation of planes* dually to the way the separation of points is calculated in Euclidean geometry. The choice is *purely a matter of consciousness*, not a mathematically determined one. We follow Adams here as his proposal arose from Steiner's research where such a space was experienced in a different state of consciousness. For this consciousness there is an *unreachable inwardness* as seen from the periphery, in contrast to our normal consciousness which experiences an unreachable outwardness as experienced from a particular point in the universe. The duality inherent in projective geometry makes all this expressible mathematically, and suggests that if the point-based approach expressed in physics by the notion of particles is so fruitful then it might be expected that the dual plane-based approach could prove equally so. This is what we wish to explore further.

For counterspace we dualize equation (1) above to give the separation between two planes:

$$\tau^2 = \frac{\left(u_0 v_3 - v_0 u_3\right)^2 + \left(u_1 v_3 - v_1 u_3\right)^2 + \left(u_2 v_3 - v_2 u_3\right)^2}{u_3^2 v_3^2} \qquad (3)$$

where u_i, v_j are the co-ordinates of two planes and τ is their separation. We will refer to τ as the *turn* between the two planes. Notice that it is not an angle, and may become infinite if one of the two planes contains the infinitely inward point O as then either u_3 or v_3 is zero. This is the dual situation to the separation of two points one of which lies in Ω. Figure 13 shows a set of planes orthogonal to the page turning about a line through equal steps in counterspace.

Each plane is separated from its neighbour by the same turn τ despite the fact that for our Euclidean consciousness they appear to be different. The *angles* are different in space, but not the turns in counterspace. The construction on the left gives a parabolic measure on the vertical axis, yielding equal steps in counterspace, which is why Adams also referred to it as *step measure*. Moving O to the Euclidean infinite plane would indeed result in Euclideanly equal steps.

The dual of (2) giving the separation of points X, Y in counterspace is

$$\cos\left(\sigma\right) = \frac{x_0 y_0 + x_1 y_1 + x_2 y_2}{\sqrt{\left(x_0^2 + x_1^2 + x_2^2\right)\left(y_0^2 + y_1^2 + y_2^2\right)}} \qquad (4)$$

where the symbol σ represents the separation which we will call *shift*. The numerator is the inner product of the non-homogeneous version of the co-ordinates of the points. We note:

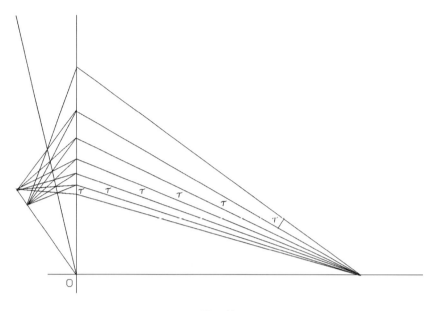

Fig. 13

1. If cos (σ) = 1 then σ = 0 and the two points lie on a line though O as OX, OY are then parallel
2. If cos (σ) = 0 then σ = π/2 and OX, OY are orthogonal

We see that σ behaves exactly like an angle, which indeed we would expect from the principle of duality we are following. In particular σ is never infinite, which takes some getting used to for points! When σ = 0 we say that *in counterspace* the two points are parallel. Two points on a line through O may be distinct and yet have zero shift, which is dual to two parallel planes in space that are distinct and yet subtend a zero angle. For the two points lie on a 'line at infinity', so called because it contains the infinitude O and is the dual of a line at infinity in space which lies in Ω.

There are no parallel planes in counterspace, only parallel points (and lines).

Parallel lines in counterspace lie in a plane through O, dual to parallel lines in space which share a point in Ω. This also requires great care as two such lines do not look parallel for our Euclidean consciousness.

Shifts may easily be visualized as equal to the Euclidean angles subtended by point-pairs in O, as summed up in Fig. 14. The points A and B are parallel, B, C are separated by a shift of 30 degrees, as are A and C, and B, D and A, D are orthogonal.

In Appendix 2 the meaning of orthogonality and the shift between lines

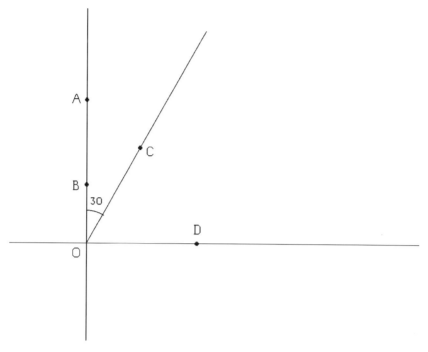

Fig. 14

is explained, and the way to calculate turns between planes is derived, which will be of use in the next chapters. The results are

Given any two planes α, β with known co-ordinates, we simply find the normalized co-ordinates of the plane ω in O and their common line, and find the turn τ between them from the relation β = α + τω

and the cosine rule for counterspace

$$\rho = \sqrt{\rho_1^2 + \rho_2^2 - 2\rho_1\rho_2 \cos(\theta_2 - \theta_1)}$$

where ρ_1, ρ_2 are the turns of two planes in from Ω, $(\theta_2 - \theta_1)$ is the shift between the lines in which they intersect Ω and equals the angle between them, and ρ is the turn between them. This is a special form of the general cosine rule for a counterspace triangle.

It is clear that the formal mathematics for counterspace is the same as that for space, with the point co-ordinates of the latter replaced by plane co-ordinates. Thus we could smile indulgently and go home, as all has already been explored in a formal sense! However, this approach would ignore the qualitatively different meaning of the mathematics, and it is just that which is of interest. For example, the restriction of transformations to polar special affine ones implies a dual quantity to volume. What is that like? How do we think about it? How do we calculate it? Does it have any significance for physics? We find that we need to get used to a different way of thinking to interpret counterspace. In the next chapters we will interpret polar area and polar volume, the duals of area and volume, having now found the basic counterspace metric quantities shift and turn.

Turns are vectors while shifts (like angles) are not. Appendix 3 explains how to resolve these vectors and find their components in counterspace.

3. POLAR AREA IN COUNTERSPACE

In the previous chapter we defined turn and shift as the fundamental metric invariants in counterspace dual to length and angle in space. We will now see how to calculate the duals of area and volume, which we will call polar area and polar volume, and see how to carry out integration. Formally differentiation and integration are no different as they do not depend upon the quality of their arguments, but their interpretation and implementation needs care. We will confine ourselves to polar area in this chapter, and work initially from first principles.

To find the area of a plane figure in space we integrate over all the points in the area, applying the metric to give lengths of line segments and angles between lines. In particular we use the metric in the latter case to define the right angle.

Thus in finding the area of a right triangle as shown in Fig. 15 we take a series of vertical lines of length y determined by the figure and metric, extend them to infinitesimal strips of width dx orthogonal to the line, define the area of the strip as y.dx, and finally integrate:

$$\text{area} = \int_0^w y.dx$$

$$= \int_0^w \left(h - \frac{h.x}{w}\right).dx$$

$$= \left[h.x - \frac{h.x^2}{2.w}\right]_0^w$$

$$= \frac{h.w}{2}$$

The points over which we integrated were all those reachable by an arbitrary point inside the triangle which moves freely provided it does not cross a side. There are four possible choices only one of which is valid, namely, that for which the point cannot go to infinity (Fig. 16).

The four projective regions A, B, C, P determined by the triangle are indicated, and only points in P can move freely without reaching infinity. To follow the dual of this process we first observe that we integrate over the planes in the polar triangle. The dual of a triangle in a plane is a line-triple in a point.

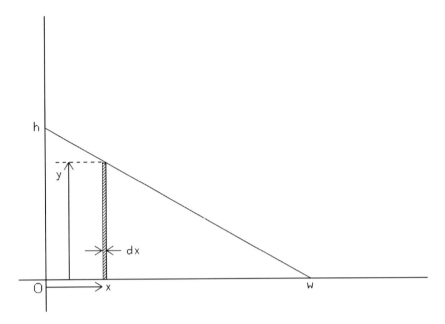

Fig. 15

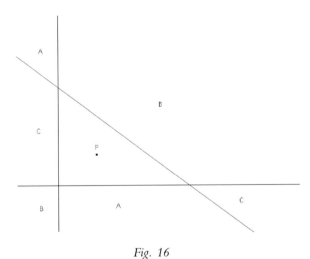

Fig. 16

The polar diagram for counterspace (Fig. 17) shows a point X and the three sides of the polar triangle XA, XB, XC.

A plane α in its polar area is shown shaded which is free to rotate about X without crossing any of the sides. The top horizontal triangle ABC is

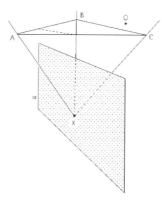

Fig. 17

shown to indicate that the infinitude O is outside the triangle such that the plane α can never contain it without crossing a side. The dotted line in ABC is its intercept with α, and it is clear that as α varies this line can never contain O. Thus of the four possible regions of the triangle, α has been chosen to lie in the one for which the polar area will be finite. We will now integrate over all these planes to obtain the polar area. We will not do this elegantly or take short cuts, but carry it out in full detail to satisfy ourselves that this way of regarding polar area in conjunction with the concepts shift and turn works satisfactorily. It will be easy to revert to simple calculation later.

First we require the polar triangle to be a right triangle, which means that two of its sides must subtend a shift of 90° in O. Thus the planes in those sides containing O must be harmonic wrt the metric cone of counterspace, i.e. they must be Euclideanly orthogonal. We take this to be the case, and to simplify our work we take the projection of the polar triangle in the plane of triangle ABC (Fig. 18):

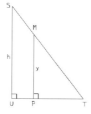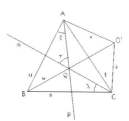

Fig. 18

On the left we show the Euclidean case and on the right the dual diagram in the plane π of ABC, so that the sides of the polar triangle intersect the plane π in A, B, C, and the intercepts of the planes are labelled s, t, u polar to S,T,U on the left. Recalling that the polar triangle lies in X (below π and not shown), OX meets π in O'. The point P on the left traverses the side UT, and the dual plane on the right intersects π in the line p through A—the point (u, t)—and rotates about AX from plane ABX to ACX. The point M on the left moves along ST as P traverses UT, and on the right the line m is the intercept of a plane in CX dual to M which moves from BCX to ACX; m and p meet in the point Q in which the line y through X intersects π, y being dual to PM = y in the left diagram. SU and PM are parallel, the dual of which is that the lines XB and XQ lie in a plane through O and hence Q lies on BO'. Thus as p varies about A it intersects BO' in Q and m is the line CQ.

The independent variable x on the left is the length of UP, the dual of which is the turn ξ between the planes ABX and AQX, shown as the arc between u and p. The dependent variable y is the length of PM the dual of which is the turn τ between CQX and AQX, shown as the arc between p and m. US and UT are orthogonal, so BX and AX are orthogonal on the right (i.e. subtend a shift of 90°). This is distorted by the projection in the above diagram. Thus QX and AX are also orthogonal, and an infinitesimal change in the turn ξ causes Q to move along BO' and hence orthogonally to AX.

We will now use suffices for the planes, so that u_i for example represents the plane co-ordinates of the plane ABX. We also need the planes-at-infinity $v_i = \text{AXO}$ and $k_i = \text{CXO}$ as shown, which are expressed in normalized form as unit vectors, so that they may be used to work with turns as parameters thus enabling us to handle turns conveniently (see Appendix 2 for an explanation of turns as parameters). The turns η between u_i and s_i, and ν between u_i and t_i, are dual to the lengths of US and UT, and are the magnitudes of the orthogonal 'sides' of the polar triangle.

First suppose that Q is momentarily fixed and we take the axial pencil of planes r_i in XQ. Then we may express the pencil as

$$r_i = p_i + \phi w_i \quad \text{where } \phi \text{ is the turn between } r_i \text{ and } p_i \text{ (as } w_i \text{ is normalized).}$$

When r_i coincides with m_i this becomes

$$m_i = p_i + \tau w_i \quad \text{as now } \phi = \tau,$$

which captures τ as a parameter for us. As r_i varies from p_i to m_i it embraces all the planes in Q which are 'inside' the polar triangle (and none of which contain O). ϕ then changes from 0 to τ so that τ is the dual of the length of PM (embracing all the points on PM). As Q moves from B along BO' until it lies on AC, we will include all the planes making up the polar area without duplication.

For the axial pencil in AX we have

$$p_i = u_i + \xi v_i \quad \text{so that } \xi \text{ is the turn of } p_i \text{ while } Q \text{ varies, being dual to}$$
$$x = UP.$$

For the axial pencil in CX we have

$$m_i = s_i + \lambda k_i \quad \text{giving the turn } \lambda \text{ from } s_i \text{ to } m_i.$$

Thus

$$s_i + \lambda k_i = p_i + \tau w_i = u_i + \xi v_i + \tau w_i$$

so

$$\tau w_i = s_i - u_i + \lambda k_i - \xi v_i \tag{1}$$

Taking the inner product of both sides by w_i (a unit vector) gives

$$\tau = (s_i - u_i)w_i + \lambda k_i.w_i - \xi v_i.w_i$$

When $\xi = \lambda = 0$ we have $\tau = \eta$, the turn from u_i to s_i, so $(s_i - u_i) w_i = \eta$, giving

$$\tau = \eta + \lambda k_i.w_i - \xi v_i.w_i$$

Now the polar triangle is the dual of a right-angled triangle, so just as y is orthogonal to UT we have the vectors (u, t) and (m, p) orthogonal, and hence

$$0 = (u_i - t_i)(m_i - p_i) = \nu v_i.\tau w_i \quad \text{since } \xi = \nu \text{ when } p_i \text{ coincides with } t_i.$$

Thus

$$v_i.w_i = 0 \text{ (which we expect for orthogonal planes)}$$

giving

$$\tau = \eta + \lambda k_i.w_i \tag{2}$$

We now need λ as a function of ξ. If we take the outer product of both sides of (1) by w_i (denoting outer products $\mathbf{x}$) we get

$$0 = (s_i - u_i)\mathbf{x}w_i + \lambda k_i\mathbf{x}w_i - \xi v_i\mathbf{x}w_i \tag{3}$$

Since

$$(s_i - u_i) = \kappa w_i \text{ for some } \kappa \text{ (as } s_i, u_i, w_i \text{ all lie in BX), } (s_i - u_i)\mathbf{x}w_i = 0,$$

and

$$v_i\mathbf{x}w_i = 1 \text{ as } v_i, w_i \text{ are orthogonal unit vectors,}$$

and

as k_i, v_i, w_i all contain OX, $k_i = bv_i$ for some b, so $k_i \mathbf{x} w_i = -bv_i \mathbf{x} w_i = -b$, (noting that w_i separates v_i and k_i, so we must use $-b$),

then substituting in (3) we get

$$b\lambda = -\xi.$$

Substituting in (2) we get

$$\tau = \eta - \xi\, k_i.w_i/b$$

Since k and w are fixed $k_i.w_i/b$ is a constant. If we set $\tau = 0$ then $\xi = \nu$ and $k_i.w_i/b = \eta/\nu$, giving

$$\tau = \eta(1 - \xi/\nu)$$

The integral is now

$$\int \tau\, d\xi = \eta\left(\xi - \frac{\xi^2}{2\nu}\right)$$

The limits are from $\xi = 0$ to $\xi = \nu$ (when $\tau = 0$), and the integral is finally

polar area $= \eta\nu/2$

which is the dual in turns of the Euclidean area $hv/2$. This shows that by integrating over all the planes 'inside' the triangle wrt to turn we indeed obtain a quantity which is the dual of Euclidean area. We stress again that we have given a detailed derivation of this from first principles to demonstrate that this approach to polar area is valid. Polar area plays such an important role later that it must be thoroughly grasped conceptually. *We conclude that we may use turns to calculate polar areas just as we use lengths for areas*, the formal proof being an appeal to the principle of duality.

Thus we see that we can integrate using turns in counterspace in the same way we integrate using lengths in space, which again we would expect from the principle of duality. Polar area, then, is the integral over all the planes making up a two-dimensional figure in counterspace. The triangle is elementary as we simply confined those planes between its sides. We will now derive the polar area $\pi\rho^2$ of a cone, the dual of the formula πr^2 for a circle in space, and see how to handle curvature. This will be of great use later in connection with light.

The dual to the plane of a circle or ellipse is the vertex of a cone, and the dual to the centre-point is a plane through the vertex. For a right circular cone the turn between that plane and any tangent plane is constant, as is the distance from the centre to the circumference of a circle. We refer to that turn as the polar radius ρ. For an elliptic cone we have the semi-major and semi-minor turns. If O lies on the axis then the centre-plane is that plane in the vertex which is orthogonal to the axis (Fig. 19).

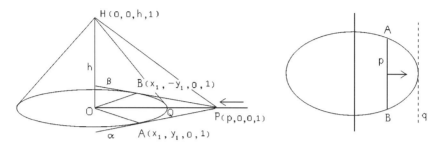

Fig. 19

We will carry out the integration for an elliptic cone. The polar area consists of all the planes through the vertex H which do not intersect the cone, dual to all the points inside the ellipse. On the right we see the integration of an ellipse, where we start from the semi-minor axis and move the chord p until it reaches the tangent at q, to give half the area. The equivalent operation in counterspace is shown on the left where we move the chord HP in to the tangent HQ in the surface, with P starting in the plane at infinity and ending at Q. OQ must be parallel to the centre plane so that HP starts in that plane, dual to the chord starting from the semi-major axis. For each position of P we find the turn between the two tangent planes α, β in HP dual to the length of the chord AB. This embraces all the planes in the axial pencil in HP which do not intersect the cone. As we move P in from infinity to Q we embrace without duplication all the planes in the polar area of half the cone.

We show the homogeneous Euclidean co-ordinates $(x_1, \pm y_1, 0, 1)$ of the tangent points A, B in a given plane parallel to the centre plane through H. The co-ordinates of the plane $\gamma = HOQ$ are $(0, 1, 0, 0)$, and those of the tangent planes α, β are

$$\left(\frac{-1}{p}, \pm \frac{x_1 - p}{p\, y_1}, \frac{-1}{h}, 1 \right)$$

This is easily verified as the inner products of this with the co-ordinates of H, P, A and B are all zero. Since γ is normalized and α, β are in Euclidean form with the last co-ordinate $= 1$, the turn τ between α and β is given by

$$\alpha = \beta + \tau \gamma$$

i.e.

$$\left(\frac{-1}{p}, -\frac{x_1 - p}{p\,y_1}, \frac{-1}{h}, 1\right) = \left(\frac{-1}{p}, \frac{x_1 - p}{p\,y_1}, \frac{-1}{h}, 1\right) + \tau(0, 1, 0, 0)$$

$$= \left(\frac{-1}{p}, \frac{x_1 - p}{p\,y_1} + \tau, \frac{-1}{h}, 1\right)$$

giving

$$\tau = \frac{2(p - x_1)}{p\,y_1} \tag{5}$$

To substitute for x_1 and y_1 we note that the tangent line through P at A is given by

$$\frac{x\,x_1}{a^2} + \frac{y\,y_1}{b^2} = 1$$

where $a = OQ$, the semi-major axis in the plane, and b is the semi-minor axis.

Since P lies in this we have

$$x_1 = \frac{a^2}{p}, \ and \ y_1 = b\sqrt{1 - \frac{x_1^2}{a^2}}$$

and substituting this in (5) and simplifying gives

$$\tau = \frac{2a\sqrt{\dfrac{1}{a^2} + \dfrac{1}{p^2}}}{b} \tag{6}$$

Now we must find the turns corresponding to the Euclidean lengths a, b and p.

The plane ϕ containing H, P and the point at infinity I on the y-axis has the co-ordinates

$$\left(\frac{-1}{p}, 0, \frac{-1}{h}, 1\right)$$

as is easily verified by the fact that its inner products with the co-ordinates of H, P and $I = (0, 1, 0, 0)$ are all zero. The centre plane ψ is parallel to the plane ABP and contains H, so it has the co-ordinates $(0, 0, -1/h, 1)$. Now a plane ϵ of the pencil with parameter μ determined by ψ and ν $(1, 0, 0, 0)$ (the YZ plane) is given by $\epsilon = \psi + \mu\nu$, so that $\epsilon = (\mu, 0, -1/h, 1)$ whence we see that for ϕ, $\mu = -1/p$. In this case we take the positive value of the turn (see Appendix 2), so it follows that the turn of the similar plane touching the cone is $1/a$ which we will define as μ_1, and the turn of the plane tangential at the extremity of the minor axis is $1/b = \mu_2$, say. Thus (6) can be properly expressed in counterspace terms as

$$\tau = 2\mu_2 \frac{\sqrt{\mu_1^2 - \mu_2^2}}{\mu_1}$$

The polar area of the cone is thus

$$\int_0^{\mu_1} \tau \, d\mu = \int_0^{\mu_1} 2\mu_2 \frac{\sqrt{\mu_1^2 - \mu^2}}{\mu_1} \, d\mu$$

$$= \left[\frac{\mu_2 \left(\mu\sqrt{\mu_1^2 - \mu^2} + \mu_1^2 \sin^{-1}\left(\frac{\mu}{\mu_1}\right) \right)}{\mu_1} \right]_0^{\mu_1}$$

$$= \frac{\pi\mu_1\mu_2}{2}$$

This is only half the total polar area, so the result is $\pi\mu_1\mu_2$, which is exactly the dual of the spatial formula πab for an ellipse. It follows that the polar area of a circular cone is

$$\pi\rho^2$$

where ρ is the polar radius, which is the turn from the centre plane through H to any tangent plane, and is the dual of the formula for a circle.

Again this has been derived in detail to show how polar area is interpreted.

A most important deduction for later work is that the polar area is independent of the position of H on the axis, so all coaxial cones sharing the same ellipse in the orthogonal plane through O have the same polar area, including the elliptic cylinder. It also follows from this that

The product of the polar area of a cone and the area of the elliptic cross-section in the orthogonal plane through O is constant.

We also record the result above that the turn of a plane rotating about a fixed horizontal line orthogonal to the vertical z-axis axis wrt the horizontal plane in that axis is

$$\frac{1}{h} \qquad\qquad (7)$$

where h is its intercept with the x-axis. This gives the above result that the polar radius is constant as the vertex moves up the z-axis (which is not apparent intuitively as the Euclidean angle is changing) so that the polar area remains constant.

Another important result for light concerns the way the polar area of a tangent cone to an ellipsoid varies.

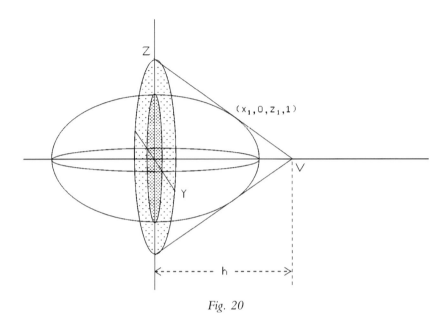

Fig. 20

If the vertex V is a distance h from the centre, and a, b are the semi-axes in the horizontal plane while c is that in the vertical plane, then the polar area of the tangent cone is, using result (7),

$$\pi \mu_1 \mu_2 = \frac{\pi}{YZ}$$

where Y and Z are the semi-axes of the cross-sectional ellipse shown. At the tangent point shown we have

$$x_1 = \frac{a^2}{h} \text{ and } z_1 = c\sqrt{1 - \frac{a^2}{h^2}}$$

from which by simple proportion we get

$$\frac{Z}{h} = \frac{z_1}{h - x_1}$$

so

$$Z = \frac{hc}{\sqrt{h^2 - a^2}}$$

and

$$Y = \frac{hb}{\sqrt{h^2 - a^2}}$$

giving a polar area

$$\frac{\pi}{YZ} = \frac{\pi}{cb}\left(1 - \frac{a^2}{h^2}\right) \tag{8}$$

For a sphere $a = b = c$ and this becomes

$$\pi\left(\frac{1}{r^2} - \frac{1}{h^2}\right) \tag{9}$$

where r is the Euclidean radius of the sphere, or in counterspace measures

$$\text{polar area} = \pi(\rho^2 - \eta^2)$$

For further work (5) suggests a useful relation for calculating turn.

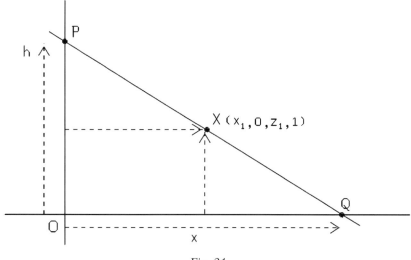

Fig. 21

Given a line p orthogonal to the vertical z-axis intersecting it in P at a height h above O, a point $X = (x_1, 0, z_1, 1)$, and a plane through p and X intersecting the x-axis in Q at a distance x from the origin, we have from (7) that the turn of the plane from the horizontal position is $1/x$. By simple proportion we have

$$\frac{h}{x} = \frac{z_1}{x - x_1}$$

$$\text{so } \tau = \frac{1}{x} = \frac{h - z_1}{x_1 h} \tag{10}$$

Thus knowing h, x_1 and z_1 for a particular problem we can find the turn.

It should be noted that in this chapter we have assumed the simple relationship that turn is the reciprocal of radial distance. This assumes a unit scaling between space and counterspace which need not be the case, as will be discussed in a later chapter.

4. POLAR VOLUME

In the previous chapter we analysed polar area. It is straightforward to extend the approach to polar volume. Given an object in space the volume is calculated by integrating over the points inside it, given a suitable metric. In counterspace we integrate over the planes making up the polar volume, which requires us to see which planes qualify. Do we mean only those planes that do not intersect the surface, and in any case what is 'surface' in counterspace?

To obtain volume in space we integrate over some suitable cross-sectional area, often in parallel planes spanning the object. For counterspace, then, we have to take 'cross-sectional areas' in points rather than planes, spanning polar-parallel points, i.e. points on a line through O. Another way to think about it is to dualize the volume of a parallelepiped as points enclosed by planes. A polar tetrahedron would be regarded in this way as planes enclosed by its vertices, so that all instances of a variable plane in a region such that the plane never traverses a vertex, and such that it never contains O, would provide a basis for integration.

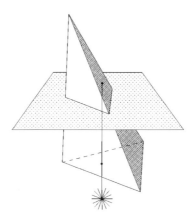

Fig. 22

The vertices are the flat 'surfaces' and we choose that region, as above (Fig. 22), in which no plane such as the shaded one can contain the counterspace infinitude O (shown as a pencil at the bottom). Then we can integrate over all the planes in that region to obtain a finite polar volume. To integrate we must choose a line through O and move the 'cross-sectional' point along that line from one boundary to another, finding the polar area for each position as in the previous chapter, and multiplying by $d\mu$ to get the element of volume. This is the definition of an element of volume polar to that for space, which is valid provided the point is varied in the polar parallel way described. All planes in each such point that lie in the chosen region are included, so that all planes of the volume are included without duplication as the point traverses the line. It starts in one face of the tetrahedron (in which there is only one plane, dual to starting at the point of contact of a tangent plane in space) and ends up at another. We will not carry this out for the tetrahedron as the procedure is quite obvious, but will proceed to illustrate it for an ellipsoid.

Polar Volume of an Ellipsoid

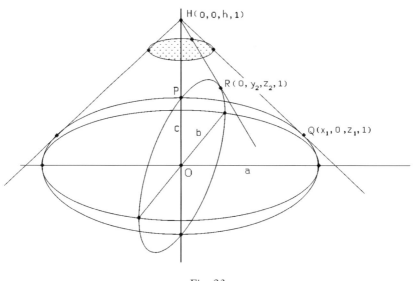

Fig. 23

A general ellipsoid is shown (Fig. 23) with the counterspace infinitude O at its centre and a tangent cone above with its vertex H on the z-axis and two profile tangent points Q and R. If we vary H from infinity in to the point P where the axis meets the surface then we fulfil the conditions required for integration, as H moves polar parallel to itself and spans half the polar volume. For each position of H we find the polar area A of the tangent cone and take the element of polar volume as $A.d\mu$. From (8) in the previous chapter the polar area of the cone is

$$\frac{\pi}{ab}\left(1 - \frac{c^2}{h^2}\right) = \pi\,\mu_1\,\mu_2\left(1 - \frac{\mu^2}{\mu_3^2}\right) \tag{1}$$

where the μ_i are the polar semi-axes, which are the turns from infinity of the tangent planes at their extremities, and the independent variable is $\mu = 1/h$.

Integrating wrt μ gives the semi-volume

$$\int_0^{\mu_3} \tau\,\mu_1\,\mu_2\left(1 - \frac{\mu^2}{\mu_3^2}\right)d\mu$$

$$= \pi\,\mu_1\,\mu_2\left[\mu - \frac{\mu^3}{3\mu_3^2}\right]_0^{\mu_3}$$

$$= \frac{2}{3}\pi\,\mu_1\,\mu_2\,\mu_3$$

and hence the full volume is twice this, which is the dual of the expression for a spatial ellipsoid. It follows that the polar volume of a sphere in counterspace with polar radius ρ is

$$\frac{4}{3}\pi\rho^3$$

and the polar volumes of the spheroids follow too.

It was essential that O was at the centre of the ellipsoid to obtain these simple dual expressions. We must now consider more carefully how quadric surfaces are classified in counterspace. Confining ourselves to real quadrics, their classification in space depends upon whether they intersect Ω in a real curve, being hyperboloids if they do, paraboloids if they touch Ω, or ellipsoids otherwise. In counterspace the dual of this provides a proper classification, so that hyperboloids possess real tangent cones with their vertices in O, paraboloids contain O in their surface, and ellipsoids have no real tangent cones in O. Examining the above figure we see that it was indeed an ellipsoid in counterspace, but had we taken O outside it (spatially speaking) then it would have been a hyperboloid, despite what our Euclidean consciousness perceives. The polar volume would then have been infinite as the tangent cone in O would have had an infinite polar area. Thus if O starts at the centre of a sphere and moves outwards the Euclidean sphere changes for counterspace first into an ellipsoid, then a paraboloid, finally becoming a hyperboloid.

On the other hand what looks like a hyperboloid for our ordinary consciousness may be an ellipsoid in counterspace if O is suitably placed. We will evaluate the polar volume of such an 'ellipsoid' to see the validity of this (Fig. 24).

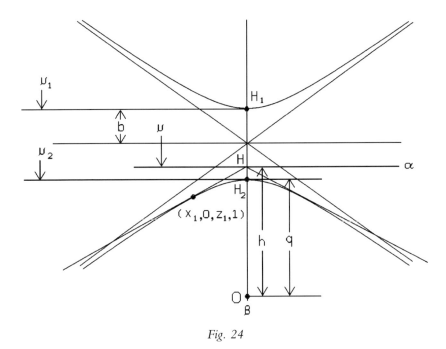

Fig. 24

Here we show the profile of a Euclidean hyperboloid with O so placed that it possesses no real tangent cone. The point H moves from H_1 to H_2 for integration. If the hyperboloid has a circular cross-section of radius r then the equation of the hyperbolic cross-section is

$$-\frac{x^2}{r^2} + \frac{(z - q - b)^2}{b^2} = 1 \qquad (2)$$

The equation of the tangent at $(x_1, 0, z_1, 1)$ is

$$-\frac{x x_1}{r^2} + \frac{(z - q - b)(z_1 - q - b)}{b^2} = 1$$

Noting that $H = (0, 0, h, 1)$ lies on it, making $x = 0$ and $z = h$, we find

$$z_1 = q + b + \frac{b^2}{h - q - b}$$

and substituting this back in (2) we get

$$x_1 = r \sqrt{\frac{b^2}{(h - q - b)^2} - 1}$$

Substituting in (10) of the previous chapter gives the turn of the tangent planes in H:

$$\tau = \frac{\sqrt{b^2 - (h - q - b)^2}}{rh}$$

Now $1/h = \mu$, and so the polar volume is given by

$$\int_{\mu_1}^{\mu^2} \pi \tau^2 \, d\mu = \int_{\mu_1}^{\mu_2} \pi \left(\frac{b^2 - (h - q - b^2)}{r^2 h^2}\right) d\mu$$

$$= \frac{\pi}{r^2} \int_{\mu_1}^{\mu^2} (-1 + 2(q + b)\mu - q(q + 2b)\mu^2) d\mu$$

$$= \frac{\pi}{r^2} \left[-\mu + (q + b)\mu^2 - \frac{q(q + 2b)\mu^3}{3}\right]_{\mu_1}^{\mu^2}$$

$$= \frac{\pi}{r^2} \left[\mu_1 - \mu_2 + (q + b)(\mu_2^2 - \mu_1^2) - \frac{q(q + 2b)(\mu_2^3 - \mu_1^3)}{3}\right]$$

Now

$$b = \frac{q + 2b}{2} - \frac{q}{2} = \frac{\mu_2 - \mu_1}{2\mu_1\mu_2}$$

$$q + b = \frac{\mu_1 + \mu_2}{2\mu_1\mu_2}$$

and the intercept of the hyperboloid with the x- and y-axes is

$$r\frac{\sqrt{q(q + 2b)}}{b} = \frac{1}{\mu_3}$$

giving

$$r^2 = \frac{(\mu_2 - \mu_1)^2}{4\mu_1\mu_2\mu_3^2}$$

Substituting for r^2, q and b in the integral and simplifying we finally get

$$\frac{2\pi}{3}(\mu_2 - \mu_1)\mu_3^2$$

Note that μ_1 and μ_2 are the turns wrt Ω of the tangent planes at H_1 and H_2, while μ_3 is the polar radius of the cylinder coaxial with the z-axis which intersects the hyperboloid in the horizontal plane β through O. From what we know about the polar radius of cones it is clear that this equals the polar radius of the cone of contact at points in β, so that all the μs still refer to tangent planes.

The above calculation can readily be repeated for the following cases:

Elliptic paraboloid with O 'inside'—identical to the ellipsoid where μ_2 and μ_3 have the same significance as for μ_3 above, and μ_1 is for the tangent plane at the umbilic.

Elliptic hyperboloid of two sheets with O suitably placed:

$$\frac{2}{3}\pi(\mu_2 - \mu_1)\mu_3\,\mu_4$$

where μ_3^2 for the circular hyperboloid becomes $\mu_3\,\mu_4$ for the elliptic cross-section.

Parabolic cone:

$$\frac{\pi}{4}\mu_1\sqrt{\mu_1\,\mu_2}$$

where in the equation of the parabolic cross-section $x^2 = -4a\,(y - q)$, $\mu_1 = 1/q$ and $\mu_2 = 1/a$.

Ruled quadrics always have a real tangent cone in O wherever it is placed, so they are always either hyperboloids or paraboloids in counterspace.

It should now be clear that great care must be taken in thinking about polar volume, and there is far more to it than a 'mere dualizing'. The following case concerning occluded volumes will illustrate this in a striking manner (see Fig. 25).

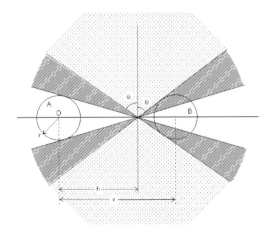

Fig. 25

O is placed at the centre of a sphere A of radius r on the left, and another sphere B of radius r on the right is an occlusion, i.e. a region excluded from the counterspace polar volume of A. B is, as seen from O, a hyperboloid in counterspace and thus has an infinite polar volume, yet paradoxically when we calculate the polar volume of A less the region represented by B we obtain a finite polar volume less than that of A alone. If h increases from r, initially the cones contribute their full polar area to the volume integral; but for values of $h > v/2$, such as that illustrated, the darker shading shows a region of the polar area that must be excluded as it contains planes that intersect B. When $h = v - r$ the whole cone is excluded, and this continues until $h = v + r$, after which increasing fractions of the polar areas of the cones contribute to the polar volume, a full contribution only being recovered when $h = \infty$. Evaluating the integral gives the loss in polar volume as

$$\frac{4\pi}{3vr^2} - \frac{4\pi r}{3(v^2 - r^2)^2}$$

where $v \geq 2r$.

Thus removing what by itself is an infinite polar volume only reduces the original by a finite amount, which illustrates the quite different nature of counterspace, there being no analogue of this in space. The reason is that a counterspace 'hyperboloid' can be 'inside' a sphere in counterspace, which is not possible in space.

The closer the two spheres the greater the reduction in polar volume, so should polar volume have practical significance this effect may be manifest as a force or other entanglement.

5. LINKING SPACE AND COUNTERSPACE

If a counterspace exists as a real part of nature then we need to see how it relates to our ordinary space. For the moment we will assume that the latter is Euclidean and postpone treating the implications of a non-Euclidean metric. Similarly we will assume that counterspace is polar-Euclidean in the sense that its metric quadric is an imaginary cone as suggested by George Adams. We distinguish the term 'counterspace' from 'polar-Euclidean space' as the former may turn out to be polar-non-Euclidean in the long term. However, we will find enough to concern us for the moment in the Euclidean case.

To establish the idea being suggested we will first propose that geometric entities can exist simultaneously in both spaces. Thus a point could represent a location both in space and counterspace, or a plane could likewise be in both spaces at once. We will refer to this as a 'linkage' between the spaces. It must be stressed that in the absence of any such linkages there is no way each space can interact with the other; they are fully independent. This is stressed because suggestions have been made that counterspace is in some sense 'the other side' of ordinary space (as its dual), a view which is not espoused here. While counterspace is dual to space, it is not in any way a part or aspect of that space in the absence of linkages.

For example, suppose a cube is linked to both spaces at its eight vertices, and the six faces are linked planes. Furthermore suppose that the counterspace infinitude is outside it as shown in Fig. 26 (lower small cube), the

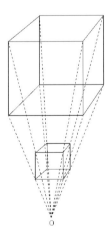

Fig. 26

dotted lines through the vertices meeting in the infinitude O. If we now translate this cube upwards from O we find that to obey the counterspace metric it must increase in size from the spatial perspective, although in counterspace its size is unaltered. This is easily seen if we recall that shifts must be invariant in counterspace transformations, and the shift separating the ends of the edges of the small cube equal those of the ends of the corresponding edges of the large one if corresponding vertices lie on lines through O.

On the other hand if the small cube moves upward and obeys the spatial metric it must remain the same size, as then lengths and angles are invariant.

It follows that the cube cannot obey both metrics at once if it is linked in the way proposed. This leads us to the first aspect of the central thesis of this book:

An object linked to both space and counterspace suffers strain when subjected to a transformation.

We are using the term *strain* in an analogous way to its use in engineering where strain is the geometric deformation caused by an impressed force. It is properly defined as the percentage change in size $\Delta L/L$ (see Fig. 27 below), but we will not insist on that for our purposes. Thus the strain on the linked cube relates to the change in size or shape suffered in one or other space as a result of the transformation.

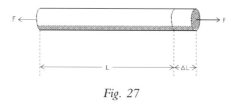

Fig. 27

Resulting from the strain on the bar above is a reactionary internal field of force called *stress*. This leads to the second aspect of our central thesis:

An object linked to both space and counterspace suffers stress as a result of an imposed strain.

We note the important difference between the purely geometrical aspect represented by the strain and the *transition from geometry to physics* entailed by introducing the concept stress. Stress and force cannot be accounted for by geometry alone, a point emphasized by Steiner (Ref. 36) and evident to common sense. The practical need for the distinction between strain and stress underlines that fact, for if the bar in the above diagram is made of steel the stress resulting from a given strain will differ from that in a similar copper bar suffering the same strain.

It is valuable to review the concept 'force', as our thesis depends critically upon it. When Sir Isaac Newton laid the foundations for classical mechanics he related force to rate of change of momentum. Now momentum entails mass, another non-geometric concept. In his theory of gravity Newton only *described* the force involved; he was unable to explain its origin beyond saying that it is engendered by mass. Einstein went further by relating it to the geometry of space itself, but his transition from geometry to force did no more than Newton had done as far as the nature of force is concerned. Generally in physics force is regarded as arising from the change of momentum of small particles such as virtual photons, so that the attractive Coulomb force between an electron and a proton arises from the exchange of negative-mass virtual photons, which impart negative momentum to the two particles and hence cause attraction. This rests upon the undefined concepts 'mass' and 'momentum'. Whether there are corresponding 'gravitons' is a subject of research.

Now the phenomenological approach is interesting. From that viewpoint we have no cause to suppose that forces act in nature because strictly speaking they are unobservable. We only observe motion, e.g. of falling apples, and the only occasion that obliges us to introduce the idea of force is when we are personally involved, e.g. in pushing a heavy object or suffering the impact of one. Thus only when our will is involved do we experience force. Then we argue by analogy that since *we* have to exert force to change the state of motion of a body, then force must act in nature when we observe objects change *their* state of motion. But that is only an analogy, for we do not observe such a force. It might be objected that we can, for example, arrange for a spring to deform when hit by a projectile, but all we will *observe* in that case will be a change in size of the spring, not a force. Again we would be arguing by analogy as *we* would have to exert a force to change the length of the spring. This is the one-sided phenomenological view, which is hard to refute.

What seems to follow reasonably from the above considerations is that *force only arises when action is impeded*, e.g. for the falling stone. Certainly we observe this ourselves, for we only experience strain and force when we try to *alter* the natural state of motion of something massive. We do not need to espouse the phenomenological view entirely one-sidedly, but its arguments do help us to see this. For a spiritual approach to physics, we are not concerned with introducing sentimentalism or in-principle vague ideas that are supposed to be 'spiritual'. Rather we note that the origin of force is quite beyond an explanation in physics as it stands, and the concept has only been acquired in the realm of being and will, namely, our own.

Where we are tempted to ascribe force to events in nature, we should remember this and either adopt the phenomenological view or else postulate the existence of *will* also in nature, if we are to remain true to observation and analogy.

The thesis proposed at the beginning of this chapter—that stress arises as a result of strain when space and counterspace are linked—is based on this idea, namely, that when we cross over from geometry to physics by invoking any of the concepts 'force', 'mass' or 'momentum' then those concepts are only needed when actions are impeded or altered, by human beings or by other agencies. We will assume that we go beyond phenomenalism only to the extent that we do not suppose human beings to be the only sources of will. We depart from solipsism in so far as we suppose other human beings also have will, and further in ascribing will to animals, and further still if we assume other agencies are active where motion is otherwise altered. This will be entailed by implication in our notion of stress, and introduces a first approach to the spiritual aspects.

The concept of strain and stress in relation to linkages has been introduced through a very simple example for a cube. It turned out as the investigation proceeded that for many purposes that example is too simple, but it is given as the bottom rung of a ladder we will attempt to climb. Before we ascend, it is interesting that the cube will suffer no strain, and therefore no stress, if it is rotated about an axis passing through the counterspace infinity at O. Only two transformations permit strain-free action: such a rotation, or a reflection. This may be related to the ubiquitous tendency we find in nature for solid objects, water and gas to end up in rotary motion, for we may presume nature will seek strain-free actions.

The problem with our 'first-rung' approach arises from the way we think about counterspace. There is no justification for assuming that there is any 'extensive' relation between the two, e.g. if a point is linked it does not follow that there is any correspondence between its distances from other unlinked points in space and the counterspace shifts between it and other unlinked points in counterspace. Indeed to suppose that is to assume that counterspace is like space in having a corresponding extensiveness. Instead it is more consistent to suppose that at each linked point counterspace appears *intensively*, in the sense that at that point a polar–Euclidean influence occurs that is only evident at that point. Likewise if a plane is linked then we might expect an orientation to be imposed on space, or be active in a tangential sense within the plane, but the angles between it and other unlinked planes in space are not relatable to turns between it and other unlinked planes in counterspace.

Next we recall the important role played by the infinite plane of space, and the infinitude of counterspace, if measurements are to be made. Without them we only have cross-ratios as invariants. So if a linkage is to have any significance both infinities must also be linked, or no 'leverage' is possible to permit effective influences to act between spaces. Forces require two points of application (fixed points or masses) to be effective, and we expect something similar for the proposed stress between the two spaces. But if the counterspace infinity is linked, then to relate it spatially to another linked point runs the same risk of borrowed extensiveness as for any other two linked points—so we do not regard *it* as linked.

One way of resolving this, adopted in this book, is to regard every linked point as an image of the counterspace infinity, which we will abbreviate to CSI. George Adams first proposed such an idea when he came to see a counterspace infinity at the growing-point of every shoot. Unless we propose millions of counterspaces to account for that insight, we need instead to see the intensiveness of one counterspace manifesting at every linked point, in the form of a CSI. Now such an idea can be seen as fractal in nature, particularly for shift which—unlike turn—is scale invariant. The notion of intensiveness is well captured by seeing an infinity at a linked point, for the spatial point is at infinity for counterspace and the rest of the counterspace is 'inward' away from the point.

To explain what is meant here by 'fractal' we will take the so-called 'chaos game' as an example. Figure 28 shows a fernlike form constructed using the Collage Theorem (see Ref. 15 for a popular account):

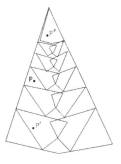 

Fig. 28

The figure on the left shows the 'tiling' used to construct the fern on the right. Each 'tile' (a shape similar to the main form) actually represents a transformation made up as follows: a translation, rotation and contraction. Thus given any starting-point P, P is regarded as belonging to the main (largest) form or space, and then one of the tiles is chosen at random (the bottom left here) and the corresponding point P' in that tile is related to it as P is to the main form. P' is then regarded as belonging to the main form, and another tile is chosen randomly (the top one here) to give P'' in a similar manner, and so the process runs. The initial 50 points are suppressed to enable the process to 'settle', and the result is the fern form on the right. The random choice of a tile on each pass has nothing to do with the fractal, but is purely a Montecarlo approach to obtain a complete picture in a reasonable time. The point of this is to see that the resulting form arises from a number of simultaneous spatial transformations, the surviving points on the fern being those which satisfy them. The Collage Theorem states that, if certain conditions are satisfied, this process yields a genuine fractal form.

We regard a number of CSIs linking the same counterspace to space as being analogous to the above tiles, the *primal* counterspace being associated with the main form. However, we do not regard the primal infinitude as itself being linked other then via the CSIs. This is only intended as an analogy to illustrate what is meant here by a fractal coupling of space and counterspace.

The kind of strain that arises for this sort of linkage is different from that for the simple case of the cube. We will refer to it as *affine strain*, and the concept is illustrated by Fig. 29:

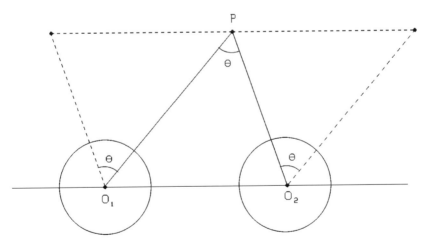

Fig. 29

Two CSIs are shown as the centres O_1, O_2 of two circles. The real meaning of the fractal quality of the linkage is that the primal counterspace sees P in different directions as viewed from O_1 and O_2. There is a directional strain indicated by the angle θ. If the linkage is metric then this angle represents a shift strain, but if the linkage is affine then shift is undefined and it indicates a directional incompatibility which we are calling affine strain as direction is an affine concept. If P moves away from the line $O_1 O_2$ then the angle θ decreases and the strain decreases, and clearly if P goes to infinity in the Euclidean sense then the strain becomes zero. As we are proposing that point linkages are CSIs, P will also be a CSI, and we see that the effect of affine strain is to cause expansion. This assumes that O_1 and O_2 are fixed and P is free to move. If all three CSIs are free to move then the situation is somewhat different and we shall see how to analyse that shortly.

There will only be movement if the strain gives rise to affine stress, and we need to see how the two are related. The problem with angles is that they are not vectors, and it is preferable to work with vectors if our results are to be independent of the co-ordinate system employed. Einstein used tensors in framing his Theory of Relativity for this reason, and we will adopt this approach too as it can only be a matter of indifference to nature what co-ordinates we use to describe her. The simplest example of a tensor is a vector such as velocity, which has a magnitude and direction which are independent of the co-ordinates used to describe it. We will see that tensors can also be found in counterspace.

For our purposes the simplest approach to affine stress is to consider the rate of change of the strain, for rate of change of angle *is* a vector. We thus propose that

Affine stress is proportional to rate of change of affine strain.

In the metric case where we have shift stress, rate of change of shift is also a vector. Mathematically the rate of change is expressed as a *gradient*, so that we will explore the proposal that affine and shift stress are proportional to the gradient of the strain.

Returning to the case of three linked CSIs, we will now analyse this idea more exactly (Fig. 30).

The three linked CSIs are shown as A, B, P and their circumcircle has been drawn, centre C. A 'sees' P in the direction represented by α, and B in the direction β. Their difference is the angle ϕ shown, which we take to represent the strain. The gradient of the strain will be a *spatial gradient of a counterspatial strain*. The gradient is a vector for which the rate of change of P is a maximum, i.e. it gives the direction in which P must move for its rate of change to be a maximum, and its magnitude is the value of that maximum. It is clear that if P moves round the circle then ϕ is constant as angles in the same segment are equal. Thus if it moves along the tangent to the circle, ϕ is instantaneously constant, so we expect the gradient to be

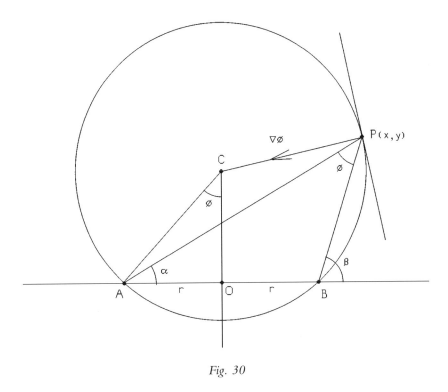

Fig. 30

orthogonal to the tangent with CP as its line of action. The magnitude is proportional to

$$\frac{AB}{AP.BP}$$

directed towards the centre C. This result for $\nabla\phi$ is proved in Appendix 4, which we will refer to as the *chord law*:

> **If three CSIs interact through shift or affine strain, then referring to their common circle, the magnitude of the strain gradient at a CSI equals the opposite chord over the product of the adjacent chords, directed towards the centre of the circle.**

The resulting stress requires a transition from geometry to physics as we have seen, and the actual value of the stress cannot be derived from the geometry alone as it depends on the physics, e.g. whether we are dealing with a gas or liquid or whatever. Thus the magnitude of the stress must be scaled to the strain by a non–geometric parameter which may be a constant or a tensor. In the case of a strained metal bar, for example, Young's Modulus which relates stress to strain is 210 GPa for steel and 117 for copper, as the same strain in each case results in a different stress. These constants have to be found experimentally. In an analogous way we will need to allow for scaling in the way space and counterspace are related.

In this chapter we have introduced the idea of strain and stress into the relationships between space and counterspace, and progressed from a simple case to a more sophisticated situation based on the fractal-type linkage proposed. As we proceed we will come across other kinds of linkage than the pointwise one introduced here. In the next chapter we will consider gravity, which was the first problem treated by this approach.

6. GRAVITATION

The idea that a strain in the linkage between space counterspace can lead to a stress that may be observable prompts the question: can we understand forces on this basis that are otherwise difficult to explain? One which immediately comes to mind is gravity. Recalling the previous chapter, we only expect a force if an action or motion is impeded.

Newton only *described* the force involved; he was unable to explain its origin beyond saying that it is engendered by mass. Einstein related gravity to geometry in his General Theory of Relativity, for if physical laws are to remain invariant under Riemannian transformations as required by that theory then we must account for the fact that acceleration at first sight seems to distinguish firmly between inertial and other frames of reference (since we experience force as a result). Einstein solved this by proposing that gravitational and inertial mass are indistinguishable, and then relating the metric of space to its mass content. If the metric is not Euclidean then the geodesics are not straight lines, so that in popular terms space is said to be curved. Einstein extended Newton's proposal that objects continue in a state of rest or uniform motion (if not acted upon by an impressed force), by saying that such objects travel along geodesics, which are not necessarily straight lines in a Riemannian space. For example, consider a stone falling towards the earth. We know that it would fall faster were it not for the atmosphere, and we say a force arises due to the resistance. But the path remains a straight line downwards. However this path is not a geodesic in the four-dimensional space Einstein used. In the absence of an atmosphere as on the moon the path *would* be a geodesic and no impeding force would then arise, but for the earth the path followed is not a geodesic and so a force arises.

Thus Einstein explains the observed *motion* of objects in this way, but he does not explain force itself. He introduced the energy–momentum tensor to describe and calculate the forces involved.

In more detail: he proposed that the element of world distance between two points is given by

$$ds^2 = g_{ij}\, dx^i\, dx^j \text{ (implied summation over repeated indices)}$$

where g_{ij} is the metric tensor and dx_i is an element of length in the four-dimensional manifold. We have a quadratic form that is invariant under the orthogonal group, and the Riemannian manifold is such that g_{ij} varies from point to point, i.e. the actual metric quadric at a point is given by the matrix $\mathbf{G}$ resulting from evaluating the elements of g_{ij} at that point. In such a manifold **G** varies, but it cannot change its type or *signature*, e.g. if it is a ruled hyperboloid at a point then it will be such everywhere. For a simple Euclidean space **G** is the unit matrix **I** everywhere, so the components of g_{ij} are constants. The substance of Einstein's approach to gravity is that the presence of mass in space causes the components of g_{ij} to become functions of position, and so the geodesics may cease to be straight lines. This accounts for the observed motion of masses when near other masses, as both are contributing to the changes in g_{ij}. As we saw in an earlier chapter, the metric of a space enables geometric measurements to be made, and g_{ij} is that (variable) metric in Einstein's case.

George Adam's proposal was that counterspace has such a metric which is an imaginary cone, i.e. it is essentially the matrix **I** but it relates to the separation of planes rather than points. We will now adopt a simple Euclidean metric for both space and counterspace and calculate the shift stress for rigid bodies. Our proposal differs from Einstein's in that the metric is not variable according to the mass content, but rather that motion results from shift strain due to a fractal linking of distinct objects, which results in a force if the action that would relieve the strain is prevented. The stress, as we shall see, is proportional to the density. For a solid we do not use the chord law, for it implies repulsion, but propose that there are two interacting CSIs at the two centres of gravity of the interacting objects, and that shift strain arises at other linked points due to the fractal nature of the linkage. This suggests that for a solid the linked points 'pool' their CSIs into one, which is significant as we shall see. A composite body composed of many parts—as all but perfect crystals are— will act through many such CSIs, and the analysis below will apply to each individually.

So we begin by considering a homogeneous solid such as a perfect crystal, referring all strain to its CSI, interacting with another CSI as shown in Fig. 31.

The circle represents a rigid spherical body with its centre of mass at C, P is the point at which shift stress is to be calculated, and O is another CSI fractally related to the CSIs making up the sphere. The shift-strain is $(\alpha - \theta)$ which is reduced if C moves towards O. As shift is not a vector we propose that the stress is proportional to the rate of change of shift strain at P.

Referring to the figure, let the strain $\alpha - \theta = \phi$ so that from the sine rule

$$\sin \phi = \frac{r.\sin \theta}{d} \tag{1}$$

Assuming d is constant and differentiating we get

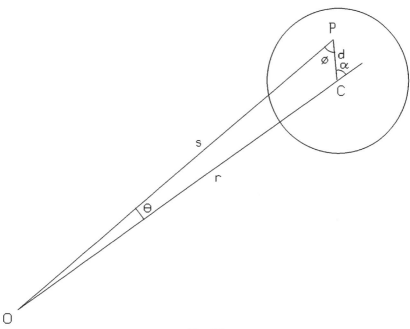

Fig. 31

$$\cos\phi \, \frac{\mathrm{d}\phi}{\mathrm{d}r} = \frac{\sin\theta}{\mathrm{d}} + \frac{r.\cos\theta}{\mathrm{d}} \cdot \frac{\mathrm{d}\theta}{\mathrm{d}r} \tag{2}$$

from which we get (noting that $\mathrm{d}\theta/\mathrm{d}\phi = -1$ for constant α)

$$\frac{\mathrm{d}\phi}{\mathrm{d}r} = \frac{\sin\theta}{\mathrm{d}.\cos\phi + r.\cos\theta} \tag{3}$$

It is easy to see that

$$\sin\theta = \frac{d.\sin\alpha}{s}$$

$$\cos\theta = \frac{r + d.\cos\alpha}{s}$$

$$\cos\phi = \frac{d + r.\cos\alpha}{s}$$

where $s^2 = r^2 + d^2 + 2.r.d.\cos\alpha$ from the cosine rule.

Substituting in (3) gives

$$\frac{\mathrm{d}\phi}{\mathrm{d}r} = \frac{d.\sin\alpha}{s^2} \tag{4}$$

This is the rate of change for the point P. If we consider all points such as P on the circle for given d and α then we multiply by the circumference $2.\pi.d.\sin\alpha$, and our expression becomes

$$\frac{d\phi}{dr} = \frac{2.\pi.d^2.\sin^2\alpha}{d^2 + r^2 + 2.d.r.\cos\alpha} \tag{5}$$

Noting that this is effectively resolved in the direction CO since we differentiated wrt r, if we now integrate with respect to α we obtain the total rate of change of strain for a spherical shell.

We integrate $\dfrac{\sin^2\alpha}{a + b.\cos\alpha}$ with respect to α and obtain

$$\frac{2\sqrt{a^2 - b^2}.\tan^{-1}\left[\dfrac{\sqrt{a - b.(\cos\alpha - 1)}}{\sqrt{a + b.\sin\alpha}}\right] + a.\alpha - b.\sin\alpha}{b^2}$$

Substituting for $a = r^2 + d^2$ and $b = 2rd$ (c.f. (5)), multiplying by $2\pi d^2$ and simplifying, we get

$$\frac{2.(r^2 - d^2).\tan^{-1}\left[\dfrac{(r - d).(\cos\alpha - 1)}{(r + d).\sin\alpha}\right] + (r^2 + d^2).\alpha - 2.r.d.\sin\alpha}{\dfrac{2.r^2}{\pi}}$$

As the integration is from 0 to π, we obtain an indeterminate value for $\alpha = 0$ but which tends to zero, and for $\alpha = \pi$ we get

$$\frac{\pi^2 \, d^2}{r^2} \tag{6}$$

i.e. we obtain the inverse square law for a spherical shell. Further it is proportional to the square of the shell radius, i.e. to its surface area, so integrating (6) with respect to d for sphere radius R gives

$$\frac{\pi^2 \, R^3}{3\, r^2} = \frac{\pi \, V}{4\, r^2}$$

So far we have analysed the rate-of-change of shift strain in the direction of the line OC, so that in effect we have resolved the total gradient $\nabla\phi$ in that direction. To convert this to stress we must introduce a suitable scaling factor as discussed earlier. What suggests itself is the density of the material making up the sphere, for if we include that at each point P in the integration then the volume V becomes the mass M. This stress will manifest if the movement of P towards O, to reduce the strain, is obstructed.

This assumption about the scaling then gives for the force

$$\frac{\pi M}{4.r^2} \tag{7}$$

so that the acceleration is proportional to $1/r^2$.

The shift strain only exists in virtue of the CSI at O, about which we have made no explicit assumptions. In particular we have not assumed a mass there. Evidently the scaling must also be affected by this CSI, or the force would be independent of it, an aspect not yet included above. The simplest proposal is that the scaling of stress to strain gradient effected via the density depends upon the scaling between space and counterspace for the CSI at O, i.e. a factor additional to the density enters in. However, we do not really know what we mean by 'density' in our present context, and it may turn out that it is itself a phenomenon associated with scaling. In fact this whole discussion suggests that.

If, however, there *is* also a massive body at O then (7) will apply to it too, and if the forces are to be equal and opposite (as we know they are from observation) then Newton's Law follows; for if we denote by k_1 the effect on C of the scaling at O, and k_2 vice versa, then (7) is multiplied by k_1 and for equal forces we have

$$\frac{\pi k_1 M_1}{4.r^2} = \frac{\pi k_2 M_2}{4.r^2}$$

which is satisfied if

$$k_1 \propto M_2$$

and

$$k_2 \propto M_1$$

This indicates clearly that 'mass' arises from the scaling between space and counterspace, as the k_i were invoked to account for it, and they end up being proportional to the opposite masses. Thus the force is proportional to the product of the masses, and the factor $\pi/4$ will be absorbed by the gravitational constant G.

For shapes other than spheres, from (4) we see that the inverse square law applies to individual points since s is the radial distance of the point itself.

For composite bodies, as remarked before, the above result applies to each part and thus to the whole. An important consequence is that gravity only applies to crystalline and other homogeneous solid bodies, which may throw light on Rudolf Steiner's research reported in Ref. 35, where he found that gravity only applies to the solid realm. The above results seem to support this, but leave open the question: what about the weight of liquids and gases? We will return to this question later.

Another consequence results from the fact that the CSI at O did not have to be a massive body. In the case of the sun, Steiner's finding that it exists in a negative space (such as counterspace) is supported since the planets—which are massive—will follow their orbits even if the sun is not massive in the ordinary sense, but simply a sufficiently 'strong' counterspace. The 'strength' refers to the scaling between that counterspace and ordinary space. If applied to stars this may lead to quite different concepts than those of black holes with their supposedly enormous masses and distasteful singularities.

In this chapter we have analysed the effect of the gradient of shift strain on two objects which each have a single CSI, and have found that Newton's Law of Gravity follows from it if the scaling between space and counterspace is related to density. The gravitational effect arises from shift strain, which is relieved if the two CSIs move closer together, but the stress is proportional to the rate of change of shift strain which increases as the two bodies move closer together. This contrasts with the viewpoint leading to the chord law in the previous chapter. Mass is, after all, scalar which may be expressed by this result. The chord law will prove to be fruitful for non-translatory transforms in gases and liquids, while gravity specifically concerns translation.

The inverse square law has been tested to high precision (Ref. 44) so the recovery of that aspect is important. The parallels and differences in comparison with Einstein's General Theory of Relativity are interesting, for while both invoke mass in a geometrical context, we see it as related to the scaling between two distinct metrics rather than the metric as such. This maintains satisfactorily the distinction between geometry and physics. A more detailed treatment to see if the specific and tested consequences of General Relativity also follow remains to be accomplished. For example, the strains and stresses between non-Euclidean space and counterspace could be investigated if the current simpler approach proves fruitful.

7. SCALING BETWEEN SPACE AND COUNTERSPACE

The previous chapters indicate the importance of the scaling between space and counterspace. What is meant by this is as follows.

Given metrics for space and counterspace, and two planes separated by a distance d (see Fig. 32), there will be a turn τ between them if they are related to a linked CSI at some point O. If the top plane moves, both d and τ vary; but we do not know by how many units of turn τ changes when d changes by one metre, say. This depends upon the scaling or calibration between the spaces, and ultimately upon the nature of the linkage.

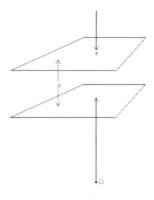

Fig. 32

The above description as it stands assumes that space and counterspace are extensively related, but the expression of scaling in terms of changes in d and τ indicates the right approach for a non-extensive linkage. We need to express the situation in tensor terms for proper generality, and we are concerned with transformations between space and counterspace, which we consider locally in the sense of Chapter 5. If the spatial Euclidean co-ordinates are x^i and the counterspace polar-Euclidean plane co-ordinates are ξ^j, then the scaling is expressed by the partial derivatives $\partial x^i / \partial \xi^j$, as in principle we can relate any x^i to any ξ^j and consider how one changes with the other.

The x^i are standard, but the ξ^j need interpreting; $\mathrm{d}x^i$ is an infinitesimal change in x^i between two points which are both infinitely far from Ω, the plane at infinity. Dually $\mathrm{d}\xi^j$ is an infinitesimal change in the turn between two planes (about an axis) both of which are infinitely 'far' from O. But, if

O is linked to a spatial point then that point is 'at infinity' for counterspace and the intensive approach sees all planes of counterspace as infinitely far from any point in space. What correspond to the three co-ordinate directions of space?

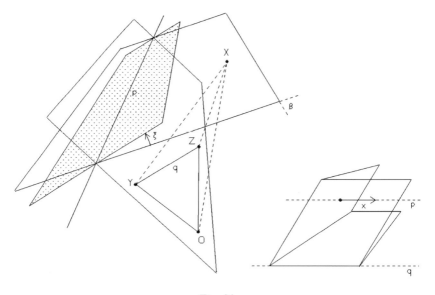

Fig. 33

For the latter we have a tetrahedron of reference made up of the co-ordinate planes together with Ω, so dually for counterspace we have a pointwise tetrahedron with O as one vertex and three other *points* as *co-ordinate points* X, Y, Z (see Fig. 33). The plane XYZ is the origin plane Γ of counterspace dual to the origin point of space. In space the co-ordinate x is the distance of a point from one co-ordinate plane along a line parallel to the other two. We use this definition, rather than the orthogonal distance from a co-ordinate plane, to maintain consistency with affine geometry, such a definition being for the so-called contravariant co-ordinate. Dually ξ is the turn of a plane about a line p *parallel* to the line q joining two co-ordinate points wrt to the plane β containing p and the third co-ordinate point. Recall that *parallel* means p and q share a common plane containing O. The diagram shows this situation.

Thus our scaling factor $\partial x^i / \partial \xi^j$ relates the rate of change of position of a point in space referred to one co-ordinate direction to that of a plane in counterspace referred to one counterspace co-ordinate *direction*. The complete scaling is thus expressed by the Jacobian matrix:

$$\begin{bmatrix} \dfrac{\partial x^0}{\partial \xi^0} & \dfrac{\partial x^0}{\partial \xi^1} & \dfrac{\partial x^0}{\partial \xi^2} \\[2ex] \dfrac{\partial x^1}{\partial \xi^0} & \dfrac{\partial x^1}{\partial \xi^1} & \dfrac{\partial x^1}{\partial \xi^2} \\[2ex] \dfrac{\partial x^2}{\partial \xi^0} & \dfrac{\partial x^2}{\partial \xi^1} & \dfrac{\partial x^2}{\partial \xi^2} \end{bmatrix}$$

which is abbreviated as $\mathbf{J} = \partial x^i / \partial \xi^j$. We use superscripts rather than subscripts to be consistent with tensor theory, which should not be confused with power indices. The determinant $|\partial x^i / \partial \xi^j|$ is called the *Jacobian*, the vanishing of which shows that the functions involved are dependent (Ref. 14). Since the x^i and ξ^j are necessarily independent this determinant must not vanish.

Unlike the scaling for gravity which is extensive, $\mathbf{J}$ expresses the scaling for local intensive scaling for non-translatory transformations such as rotations and reflections. Thus if we have a gradient $\nabla \phi$ in space such as that for the chord law, we can transform it to counterspace thus

$$\nabla \sigma = \mathbf{J} \nabla \phi$$

as gradients are covariant. This is just what we would expect, as the corresponding counterspace gradient must relate to the spatial one via the scaling of the two spaces.

8. STATES OF MATTER AND THE FOUR ELEMENTS AND ETHERS

Classically matter was considered to exist in four states: fire, air, water and earth. Today we would instead refer to these as heat, gas, liquid and solid, the difference being that heat is no longer regarded as an independent state of matter. The consideration of different kinds of geometry gave us the following broad classification:

Projective geometry
Affine geometry
Special affine geometry
Metric geometry

Special affine geometry shows that volume is a quantity independent of length as it is conserved there, even though the ratios of the lengths of the sides of an object are not invariant. We know that this characterizes liquid in the sense that a liquid is virtually incompressible. Clearly metric geometry well characterizes crystals and the solid state in general, so we suggest that affine geometry characterizes gas. This is quite reasonable as it allows expansion—a notable quality of gases. In our context we do not suppose that there are different *spaces* of these kinds, but rather that linkages between metric space and polar-metric counterspace can have these qualities, so that in the case of solids the linkage is fully metric while for liquids and gases it is affine. We do not extend this notion to heat and relate it to projective geometry, since measurements of temperature and heat are possible yet projective geometry allows no measurements as it does not leave any infinitude invariant. Perhaps this reflects the change in status of heat in science today! In some ways energy seems to play the role of fire as conceived by the ancients. We will return to this question at the end of this chapter.

If a linkage is not fully metric then the spaces behave like affine spaces for that linkage. If space *dominates*, for example, we assume that all strain is suffered by counterspace. For gases, liquids and solids we will—encouraged by the result for gravity—assume pointwise linkages for which space dominates. In the case of gravity we did not permit any expansion in calculating the strain, and only looked at translation to relieve it. This illustrates the idea that the strain was metric in counterspace, and so it was shift strain rather than affine strain; we had a fully metric linkage in which space dominated. For gas we expect an affine linkage for which space dominates, and for liquids a special affine one. We note that we are free to use angles, lengths, shifts and turns for the geometry as the spaces them-selves remain metric, but the *linkage* is affine so the strain acts within affine freedoms and constraints. This means that transformations to relieve the strain act thus. For fractally linked CSIs it controls whether they may act expansively or not, for example. Thus in deriving the chord law we used spatial angles but we did not use shift to calculate the magnitude of the stress, defining instead affine strain and stress.

The other obvious possibility is that counterspace dominates the linkage and the strain is spatial. Such linkages will evidently have an entirely dif-ferent quality, and we will explore the possibility that they relate to the *four ethers* discovered by Rudolf Steiner (Ref. 34). That implies they relate to light, chemistry and life, heat again needing to be treated specially. Prompted by Steiner's findings that gas and light originated together—as did liquid and chemistry, and solid and life—we will examine the possi-bility that an affine linkage with counterspace dominant describes light, a special-affine linkage chemistry, and finally a metric one with counterspace dominant, life. We can then sum up our total proposed picture of science in relation to space and counterspace in Fig. 34:

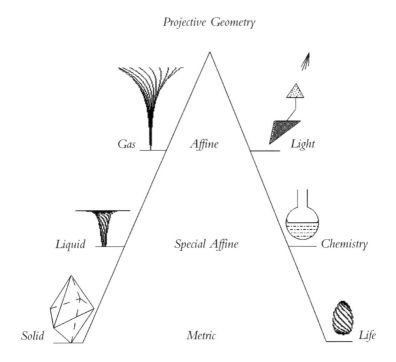

Fig. 34

This is intended to illustrate that we seek a complete picture, not just a few *ad hoc* results, but at the present stage of development the project is incomplete, and is developing iteratively to find how the seven different aspects above—heat, gas, liquid, solid, light, chemistry and life—help us to complete the picture in a consistent manner. Thus the approach to gravity imposes constraints, as will other areas, that are helpful and provide guidance. It will be important to include other aspects such as sound, electricity, magnetism and quantum phenomena.

Finally we need to return to heat. The basic phenomenon we will start with is that when a solid is heated it expands. This is a non-metric transformation in the strict sense, although some definitions of metric geometry (e.g. Ref. 27) permit similarity transformations. We do not accept this definition here, which only results if the route to metric geometry via special affine geometry is not taken, and Cayley's approach is adopted instead which leapfrogs the affine and proceeds directly from projective to metric geometry. The whole logic of our approach demands that the expansiveness implicit in a similarity transform is not to be included in metric transformations. Having said this, the expansion of a solid on heating suggests a change in the way space and counterspace are related, i.e. a change in the scaling. This prompts us to adopt as our initial approach to heat that it controls the intensive scaling of space and counterspace. That is, the Jacobian $|\mathbf{J}|$ is altered when the temperature changes. We will leave open the details for the moment, e.g. is it purely the determinant of $\mathbf{J}$, or its leading diagonal that is affected by heat? We will return to this in Chapter 12. We note also that this accords with the trivial phenomenon that heat does not cause translation, and so can only affect the intensive scaling which excludes that. Equally it accords with the phenomenon that gravity is unaffected by heat, at least if we ignore relativistic effects which are in any case minute. Thus if we heat an iron bar its total energy content increases but the relativistic change in mass is negligible compared with what we might expect if the scaling affected gravity.

9. GASES

In this chapter we will explore the proposal that a gas is described by an affine pointwise linkage between space and counterspace for which space dominates and the strain exists in counterspace. The basic phenomenon that guides us is the expansive nature of gas, and how it is affected by heat. We start from the assumption that counterspace is fractally related to space in the intensive sense described in Chapter 6, and examine the consequences of applying the chord law to an enclosed sphere of gas. Steiner (Ref. 35) described a 'tearing of space' when lightning occurs, and he also described the space inside the sun as negative (Ref. 37), and we will now extend the idea of tearing to the surface of the sun such that the fractalization of a gas represents a 'tearing' of its primal counterspace. This tearing manifests on the surface of the sun as the wonderful corona, and accounts for the gases detected in the sun's surface.

Returning to the chord law, we note that measurable physical effects only occur where a linkage is rendered fully metric, so we expect to find gas exerting its influence on its metric boundaries where it interacts with a metric object, e.g. the walls of a container. In the purely affine state it is difficult to say where the linked CSIs *are* since length is not an absolute invariant: the distance between two linked CSIs is not an invariant. We suggest that this affine quality replaces the atomistic picture of little massive atoms flying about with a mean free path. Indeed we go further and suggest that the kinetic theory works *because* it pictures in a materialistic manner what is really an affine state. However at the walls of a container interactions occur which 'metrize' the gas there, just as a measurement forces its object into a measurable state—renders it *metric*. Thus measurement can be regarded as forcing a transition from the affine to the metric, and if the two are not consistent then that aspect of the situation becomes metric which the conditions require, and other aspects then become unmeasurable. We are reminded of Heisenberg's Uncertainty Principle, to which we will return in another chapter.

Figure 35 shows a cross-section of a spherical container filled with gas, the latter being denoted by points to represent the CSIs involved (not atoms).

We take a triangle with sides r, s, t as shown and with two of its vertices lying on the inside wall of the container, the third lying inside the body of the gas. We suppose the inside radius of the sphere to be R. This represents a triangle with two CSIs undergoing metric interactions with the wall, and we now apply the chord law to this triangle. We do not consider non-

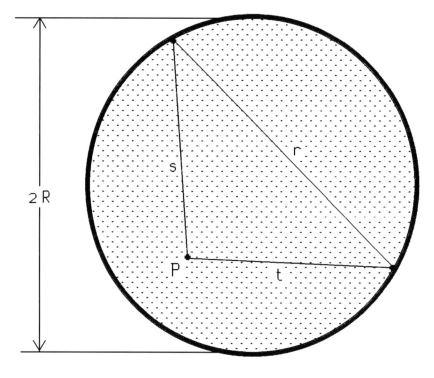

Fig. 35

planar configurations of CSIs such as tetrahedra since the linkage is affine and so we can only compare quantities in one counterspace direction, i.e. in one plane at a time. We see that for P there is an affine strain with gradient $\nabla\phi$, noting that the other two CSIs are momentarily anchored due to their interaction with the wall so that this strain *is* effective for P (c.f. Chapter 5). We recall from the chord law that

$$\nabla\phi = \frac{r}{s.t}$$

For a given such triangle $r/(s.t) \propto 1/R$, which will clearly be true for all such triangles.

Now we need to sum the total effect of all possible triangles. We assume that the number of interacting CSIs on the surface is approximately fixed in relation to the volume as every CSI such as P which is not on the surface suffers repulsion from the wall due to its membership of many triangles, and so overall the gas strives to fill the whole volume. Thus as the volume changes the number of interacting CSIs on the wall remains constant on average, so $\nabla\phi$—the total of all individual $\nabla\phi$s—is inversely proportional to R. Now we recall that we defined the shift stress as being proportional to $\nabla\phi$, so the total *stress* due to the interaction with the wall is inversely proportional to R. The pressure is this total stress divided by the surface area $4.\pi.R^2$, so the pressure is inversely proportional to R^3. Thus we deduce Boyle's Law: $PV = $ constant for ideal gases.

Some scaling factor is involved when we convert $\nabla\phi$ into stress, and the resulting pressure involves this factor. We proposed in Chapter 8 that the intensive scaling between space and counterspace is affected by heat, in which case that factor and hence P is proportional to the temperature T, and we can write

$$PV = kT$$

the ideal gas law. The relation between k and the gas constant R should yield quantitative information about the scaling tensor **J**.

We have supposed that a given quantity of gas involves a given number of fractally linked CSIs. This will provide a basis for rethinking Avogadro's constant in terms of the linkage density instead of a number of atoms. However, we do not say that atoms never exist, but rather that they may 'metrize out' of the affine aggregate of CSIs when interactions occur, but are 'reabsorbed' into that aggregate when no longer in metric interaction. As an analogy, consider a fixed torch being switched on and producing a Maltese-cross shaped figure on the wall. The proportions and area of this cross may be determined, after which the torch is turned off. If the torch is turned on again the same cross will be produced and the previous measurements will prove repeatable. However that repeatability does not prove that the cross existed on the wall throughout, and no more do repeatable measurements of the properties of atoms prove that they exist continuously between such measurements. This seems well in line with the way interactions are conceived in quantum physics, a topic to which we will return. In the affine aggregate CSIs have non-fully determinate locations, enhancing the fluid quality of the gas.

We also notice that in our analysis we have not made any assumptions about the nature of the gas involved, which is indeed true of the ideal gas law which applies to all gases. But we *have* assumed that the scaling constants are the same for all gases, which is reasonable as the scaling relates space and counterspace for general linkages. The involvement of density in the case of the gravitational scaling may require a small correction when we see how to relate gravity to gases, a possibility not so far treated as our approach to gravity apparently only applies to metric linkages.

We also note that we have taken account neither of the effect of the walls of the container in producing hybrid triangles nor of the effects of small triangles away from the walls engendering stress due to the interactions of their vertices with the wall. The effect is likely to be small, but greatest for small triangles due to the inverse relation between linear size and stress. A proper allowance for these effects may yield the van der Waal's corrections.

Finally we emphasize the important role played by the assumption that the affine stress is proportional to the gradient $\nabla\phi$ of the strain. This broad assumption—that stress is proportional to gradient—has worked well both for gravity and gases, in the one case for shift stress and in the other for affine stress.

10. LIQUIDS

The analysis of gases in the previous chapter suggests that for special affine linkages a similar approach may be adopted, but now exploiting the constant-volume properties allowed by that linkage. Thus we may for simplicity take a tetrahedron and apply the chord law to its faces, and see how it behaves if the tetrahedron is constrained to maintain its volume constant.

A simple way of handling a constant-volume tetrahedron is to note that if one triangle is fixed—in a plane α—and the opposite vertex moves in a plane parallel to α then the volume is constant. This is analogous to the theorem that triangles on the same base and between the same parallels have the same area.

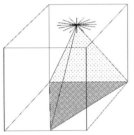

Figure 36 illustrates this, where the tetrahedron has been embedded in a cube for convenience. If the top vertex moves in the top plane of the cube then the volume remains constant. The other vertices may move in a similar manner, parallel to their respective opposite bases, to maintain constant volume.

Fig. 36

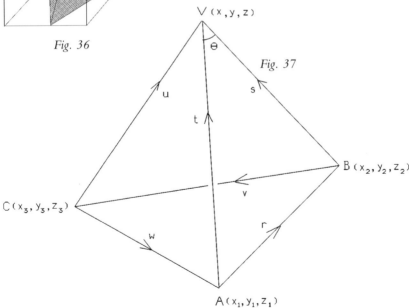

Fig. 37

Figure 37 shows a tetrahedron with sides as vectors and vertices with their appropriate co-ordinates. For the affine strain at the top vertex V in the triangle ABV, we find the following expression (see Appendix 5 for the full analysis):

$$2\,A_1\frac{\partial\theta}{\partial x} = \frac{s_x\mathbf{s.r}}{s^2} - \frac{t_x\mathbf{t.r}}{t^2} \tag{1}$$

where A_1 is the area of triangle ABV, bold type indicates the vector with the sense shown in the diagram, non-bold type indicates the magnitude, and e.g. s_x means the x-component of $\mathbf{s}$. If we vectorially add the three strains at V for this and the other two triangles we get

$$\frac{\partial\theta}{\partial x} = \frac{s_x l + t_x m + u_x n}{2(A_1 + A_2 + A_3)} \tag{2}$$

where

$$
\begin{aligned}
l &= \mathbf{s}.(\mathbf{r} - \mathbf{v})/s^2\\
m &= \mathbf{t}.(\mathbf{w} - \mathbf{r})/t^2\\
n &= \mathbf{u}.(\mathbf{v} - \mathbf{w})/u^2
\end{aligned}
$$

Since l, m, n are independent of the co-ordinates we see that partial differentiation wrt y and z gives the same result, except that the x suffices are replaced by y and z suffices respectively, so vector addition of $\partial\theta/\partial x$, $\partial\theta_2/\partial y$ and $\partial\theta_3/\partial z$ gives the total gradient at V as

$$\nabla\phi = \frac{l\mathbf{s} + m\mathbf{t} + n\mathbf{u}}{2(A_1 + A_2 + A_3)} \tag{3}$$

using ϕ to denote the combined shift at V. θ_2 and θ_3 are the angles at V in the other two faces. This is the total gradient, but to satisfy the constant volume constraint we must resolve it parallel to the face ABC. The result, using $\nabla\sigma$ for the resolved gradient, is

$$\nabla\sigma = \frac{[\mathbf{h}\,\mathbf{X}\,(l\mathbf{s} + m\mathbf{t} + n\mathbf{u})]\,\mathbf{X}\mathbf{h}}{2(A_1 + A_2 + A_3)} \tag{4}$$

where $\mathbf{h}$ is the unit vector normal to ABC and $\mathbf{X}$ is the outer product operator. This can also be expressed as

$$\nabla\sigma = \frac{(\alpha\mathbf{r.v} + \beta v^2 + \gamma\mathbf{v.w})\mathbf{r} - (\alpha r^2 + \beta\mathbf{r.v} + \gamma\mathbf{r.w})\mathbf{v}}{8\,A_4^2(A_1 + A_2 + A_3)} \tag{5}$$

where

$$
\begin{aligned}
\alpha &= (\hat{\mathbf{s}}.\mathbf{v})^2 + (\hat{\mathbf{t}}.\mathbf{w})^2 + (\hat{\mathbf{u}}.\mathbf{v})(\hat{\mathbf{u}}.\mathbf{w})\\
\beta &= (\hat{\mathbf{s}}.\mathbf{r})^2 + (\hat{\mathbf{u}}.\mathbf{w})^2 + (\hat{\mathbf{t}}.\mathbf{r})(\hat{\mathbf{t}}.\mathbf{w})\\
\gamma &= (\hat{\mathbf{t}}.\mathbf{r})^2 + (\hat{\mathbf{u}}.\mathbf{v})^2 + (\hat{\mathbf{s}}.\mathbf{r})(\hat{\mathbf{s}}.\mathbf{v})
\end{aligned}
$$

with $\wedge$ denoting unit vectors

This formulation is more obviously parallel to the plane ABC as the two terms in brackets in the numerator are scalars, and **r** and **v** lie in ABC.

These equations govern how the tetrahedron behaves if the stress is proportional to $\nabla\sigma$. We may make some deductions from them.

Referring back to (3) we see that if the faces ABV, ACV, BCV of the tetrahedron are congruent then $s = t = u$, so $l = m = n$, and hence $\nabla\phi$ is directed upwards orthogonal to ABC, making $\nabla\sigma = 0$. In particular this is true if the tetrahedron is regular. Thus we expect the stress to transform the tetrahedron into a regular one as the stress on A, B and C is non-zero.

Equation (3) also shows most clearly that the gradient is inversely proportional to the linear size of the tetrahedron, for l, m, n are independent of the co-ordinates, **s**, **t**, **u** are proportional to its linear size, and the A_i are proportional to the square of the linear size. In other words, $\nabla\phi$ is inversely proportional to the radius of the circumsphere for fixed proportions. Applying similar considerations to (5) shows the same is true for $\nabla\sigma$. We deduce from this that the smaller the tetrahedron the larger the stress, so the effects of affine strain are greatest at short ranges. However, it is noteworthy that there are long-range effects also.

For a long thin symmetrical tetrahedron such as that shown in Fig. 38 the gradient is greatest at A, B and C and zero at P. This is most readily seen in equation (1) as the inner products in the numerator vary directly with θ, and from (3) the unresolved gradient at P is orthogonal to the base. Thus the effect of the stress is to draw the base ABC towards P. A computer simulation of (5) verified this. The consequence is that in a drop of water there will be many such tetrahedra with small bases in the surface and their fourth vertex inside the drop, so the surface will tend to be drawn inwards, which accounts for the tendency of a drop to become spherical. Generally it is clear that near the middle of a volume of liquid the effects of stress on tetrahedra tend to balance out, the imbalances being greatest at the surface. In particular for small tetrahedra at the surface—for which the stress is greatest—there will arise a strong 'surface effect'.

Fig. 38

The smallest tetrahedra suffer the greatest stress and hence will tend to hold their shape as regular tetrahedra, the effect falling off with size. This may account for the short-range structure that tends to arise in water, for example. Inside a volume of liquid the total stress on a CSI is never zero although it tends to be most balanced in the centre. This indicates the 'sensitive' quality of a liquid as it is never in a state of zero stress and is continuously responsive to changes. This can be related to the phenomenon that after a volume of liquid in a container has been shaken or otherwise disturbed it takes some considerable time to settle.

In a tetrahedron as shown in Fig. 39 the side AB is long compared with QP, and QP is very close to AB without intersecting it. The gradient is least at A and B and greatest at Q and P. The result, verified by simulation, is that QP tends to rotate about AB, and A and B move only very slowly towards QP. Great care in setting up Q and P symmetrically failed to prevent the rotation. A and B were observed to move in spirals as shown below:

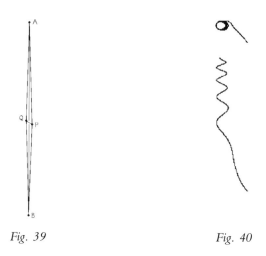

Fig. 39   Fig. 40

Figure 40 (upper) shows the plan view of the movement of a vertex such as A and the lower figure shows the elevation as it moves down towards QP in a spiral. B moves upwards in a similar spiral. Their movement is slow as the stress on A and B is small compared with that on Q and P. QP rapidly assumes a direction orthogonal to AB and then rotates. This indicates a possible source of vorticity in the liquid. It will be especially effective for very long tetrahedra with small volumes (as then the stress at Q and P is greatest), which seems to relate well to that phenomenon.

If the tetrahedron is flat, i.e. with zero volume, then after a settling period it behaves chaotically. While such behaviour will be damped by other forces away from the surface, *in* the surface flat tetrahedra will exist and such behaviour could account both for Brownian motion and evaporation. The latter is interesting from the geometrical aspect as area is not an invariant for three-dimensional special-affine geometry, so it is—on the present view—'gas' like, which indeed relates well to evaporation.

If two liquids are mixed then we have the possibility of hybrid tetrahedra, and the resulting behaviour will depend upon whether the stress is greater or less for a hybrid tetrahedron compared with a homogeneous one. In the former case the liquids will tend to mix as hybrid tetrahedra will hold together more readily than homogeneous ones, while in the latter case the liquids will tend to be immiscible.

It is clear that shear effects are particularly significant in liquids in view of the constant-volume property, so the off-diagonal components of the scaling tensor $\mathbf{J}$ will assume particular importance in converting strain to stress. This indicates that the viscosity will be affected by the scaling, and hence the temperature, as is observed. Generally temperature will affect the rate at which the above outlined behaviours take place as the magnitude of the stresses involved will be affected. This we expect. As for solids the temperature will change the volume, and it should be borne in mind that when we consider the constant volume properties of liquids we of course assume constant temperature.

An important aspect of water is its microstructure. At short ranges tetrahedral crystals form which are not stable. This might be expected as we have seen that the affine stress is greatest at short ranges for a tetrahedral group of CSIs.

A question left open in Chapter 6 concerned the weight of liquids and gases as gravity only operates where the CSIs of an object are 'pooled'. Now that we have introduced the fractal nature of gases and liquids composed of CSIs, we recall from Chapter 6 that of the two CSIs concerned in gravitational attraction no assumptions had to be made about one of them other than that it was linked and thus scaled to space. Thus when the earth attracts the atmosphere it interacts with all the CSIs of the gases individually to give them weight, and similarly for the CSIs of a liquid. The 'pooling' remains an important subject of investigation as we seek to integrate the various aspects of this book into a whole.

The simple nature of our assumption for treating liquids, namely, the mere analysis of strain gradient for constant-volume tetrahedra, leads to a surprising number of qualitative conclusions that seem to accord well with observed phenomena. This simple analysis needs to be taken much further, with multi-tetrahedron models and an attempt to derive such results as the Navier–Stokes equation. It does, however, seem a promising beginning.

11. FORCES

The analysis of gravity, gases and liquids has shown the fruitfulness of assuming a fractal linkage of CSIs and relating the stress to the gradient of the strain, either shift or affine strain. Furthermore it was important in the analyses that the stress was—ignoring temperature changes—proportional to the gradient. As we seek the best way to see how the basic proposal that linkages lead to stress and strain should relate to phenomena, we take the results so far as an important guide. Thus we now firmly adopt the following proposals for pointwise linkages:

> The stress is proportional to the gradient of the strain for constant temperature.
> Counterspace is linked to space fractally, in the sense we have adopted. The scaling between space and counterspace is determined by the temperature, and for non-translatory transformations is expressed by the hybrid Jacobian matrix $\mathbf{J} = \partial x^i / \partial \xi^j$.
> It is valid to use hybrid tensors such as $\mathbf{J}$ that relate to both spaces.

We calculated $\nabla \phi$ in space in each application, i.e. we found the spatial gradient of a counterspace strain. However, we uncritically took the stress to be proportional to $\nabla \phi$ without enquiring further as to the nature of the stress: is it a vector in space or counterspace? The derivation of the ideal gas law from Boyle's law depended critically on the assumption that scaling affects the transition from geometry to physics in relating the gradient to stress and thence pressure. In liquids we saw a similar importance. Furthermore we saw that $\mathbf{J}$ is the most natural way of capturing this idea mathematically. But $\mathbf{J}$ was defined for the transformation of covariant vectors from space to counterspace (although it could also transform contravariant counterspace vectors to space). Thus the implied use of $\mathbf{J}$ in obtaining the stress has the consequence that the result is a counterspace planar vector, not a spatial vector. This accords to some degree with the work of George Adams who first proposed that forces could be regarded as counterspace vectors (Ref. 3). He demonstrated how the use of these vectors gives the trihedral and tetrahedral laws for calculating the resultant of several forces.

However our approach extends this idea from position vectors to vector fields, and regards the force not as turn directly but as the gradient of turn. It seems sensible to explore this, as stress is often a tensor field of higher order than a vector. As things stand the stress will be covariant in counterspace, for we have

$$\mathbf{J}\, \nabla\phi = \frac{\partial x^i}{\partial \xi^j}\, \frac{\partial \phi}{\partial x^i} = \frac{\partial \phi}{\partial \xi^j}$$

so that $\mathbf{J}\nabla\phi$ is clearly covariant. As the result equates to a counterspace turn vector we write $\mathbf{F} = \partial\sigma/\partial\xi^j$ for some counterspace scalar field σ in place of ϕ. While we remain with orthogonal polar-Euclidean counterspace this does not matter, but its implications are interesting as usually force is most naturally regarded as a contravariant vector in space. Another possibility is that the gradient $\partial/\partial\xi^j$ needs—to be regarded as a force—to be converted to contravariant form using the counterspace metric tensor, i.e. we 'raise the suffices' in the usual tensor manner. Again this is trivial mathematically in polar-Euclidean space where the metric tensor is the constant unit matrix $\mathbf{I}$, but the quality of the vectors is what is interesting. When we consider light we will find these distinctions to be of great importance.

Thus we conclude along with George Adams that force is a counterspace planewise vector, although we go further and postulate it is the gradient of a counterspace scalar field.

We need to examine $\mathbf{J}$ a little more closely, as so far we have only defined it in very general analytic terms. What sort of quantities are the components $\partial x^i/\partial\xi^j$? In our analysis of liquids and gases we assumed a strict proportionality between stress and $\nabla\phi$. Thus although $\mathbf{J}$ transforms $\nabla\phi$ to counterspace to yield stress, we have otherwise expected it to behave like a proportionality constant for constant temperature. This is achieved if the $\partial x^i/\partial\xi^j$ are constant for constant temperature, and we will assume this, i.e. $\partial x^i/\partial\xi^j = k^i_{\ j}\,(T)$ where the $k^i_{\ j}$ are functions of T which are constant for a given T. However we expect them to depend upon the substance involved as changes in T do not affect all substances to the same degree, so that copper and lead, for example, will have different values for the $k^i_{\ j}$ as they expand by different amounts when heated. This is interesting as it means that within a particular substance we find a characteristic scaling of space to counterspace. This will prove of significance when we study refraction, as the scaling of space and counterspace changes at a boundary between air and glass, for instance, yielding Snell's Law.

Semple and Kneebone (Ref. 27, page 200) mention the fact that the algebraic approach to projective geometry fails to reflect the symmetry of the subject, as a point transformation $\mathbf{x}' = \mathbf{P}\mathbf{x}$ induces a plane transformation $\mathbf{u}' = \mathbf{P}^{-1\mathbf{T}}\mathbf{u}$ but the elements p_{ik} of $\mathbf{P}$ enter differently into the two equations. They then embark upon a discussion of concomitants, covariants and contravariants, but they do not discuss mixed concomitants. But we are clearly concerned with mixed concomitants in our use of $\mathbf{J}$ as a hybrid tensor. We assume this to be valid.

We must now return to the question of the scaling for translations. The force of gravity cannot be related to **J** as it is independent of temperature. The most likely approach seems to be to relate **J** to intensive rotary linkages, and seek another scaling tensor for translations first, and then rigid rotations. In analysing gravity we also assumed that the stress was directly proportional to the strain gradient. Also we only used one CSI for each body, which seems to imply an extensive linkage in contrast to the intensive one used for affine stress. In approaching this more closely we must ask what the most essential feature of translation is *physically* as opposed to merely geometrically. Bare movement is geometric, but the physical aspect surely seems to relate to momentum, for changes in motion of real objects always entail changes in momentum. The stress in these cases is rate of change of momentum, and the transition from geometry to physics necessarily brings it in. Now momentum is a vector, so $d\phi/dx$ is proportional to the rate of change of a vector, which is not a gradient, in line with the fact that we did not use the gradient for gravity, but a particular rate of change. Initially we shall find it more suitable to work with *impulse*, which is defined as force multiplied by time. Impulse has the same dimensions as momentum, i.e. MLT^{-1}, showing the relation between the two. An example may be useful. If a stone with a definite momentum hits a window then the momentum determines the impulse $\int F.dt$ applied to the glass. If the momentum is not too great the time taken to stop the stone—determined by the force the glass can exert—is short enough to avoid sufficient deformation to break the glass. The greater the momentum the greater the impulse until breakage occurs. Thus another way of thinking about momentum is to regard it as the time for which a body can apply a definite force before being brought to rest. Before looking at the consequences of this, it is useful to review the concept of potential.

The so-called gravitational potential is a fictional scalar field useful for calculation, of which the gravitational force is regarded as the gradient. This potential field is radial so we could instead regard the rate of change of shift strain as the gradient of a suitable potential, which would then require it to act from centre to centre. But can we give a proper meaning to 'potential', other than as a fiction? An obvious idea in line with our basic thesis is to see it as a strain between space and counterspace, and of course the rate of change of shift strain relates to gravity, so that would relate potential to shift strain. An immediate apparent problem lies in the fact that shift strain *increases* radially whereas conventionally the potential decreases, being proportional to $1/r$. However, there may be some sense in that, as the further away a body is, e.g. from the earth, the *greater* is its potential energy (although we recognize that potential energy is a different concept). Our proposal sees the fall off in gradient with separation as due to the fact that the angle expressing shift strain grows rapidly with initial separation, and then ever more slowly, whereas conventionally the potential actually decreases with radius to achieve the same effect on the gradient. Our approach has the merit that the potential has a real basis apart from its gradient, i.e. as being proportional to an actual strain, and also that it reflects the physical fact that the further away a body is the greater its potential impulse or momentum if it falls down to a given reference level. When we transform the gradient to stress we again transform a spatial gradient into a counterspace vector, but this cannot be a distance-to-turn transformation as we have already accounted for *that* scaling with **J**. To approach this we can seek an interpretation of shift. What are its 'units' if not degrees? In other words, is there a non-geometric quantity measured by the geometric concept shift, corresponding to the transition from geometry to physics? From what we have said above it seems reasonable to propose that the required scaling relates impulse to strain, in which case shift measures the physical quantity impulse, or more strictly potential impulse. Now impulse is a vector but shift is a scalar, and for scaling purposes we need something analogous to $\partial x^i / \partial \xi^j$ used for **J**, so recognizing that the impulse is necessarily radial we can give it the form $g = k \partial I / \partial \phi$ where I is the magnitude of the impulse and k is a constant.

We can express $d\phi/dr$ as a gradient suitable for potential by seeing it as the only non-zero component $\partial \phi / \partial r$ in polar co-ordinates (r, θ, ψ), since for the gravitational shift strain $\partial \phi / \partial \theta = 0$ and $\partial \phi / \partial \psi = 0$. Its direction is $\hat{\mathbf{r}}$, the unit vector in the radial direction, so for gravity $\nabla \phi = \hat{\mathbf{r}} \partial \phi / \partial r$. Similarly we can express the force $d\mathbf{I}/dt = \hat{\mathbf{r}} \partial I / \partial t$. We can then relate all this to the force $\nabla \sigma = d\mathbf{I}/dt$ as follows

$$\mathbf{F} = \nabla \sigma = d\mathbf{I}/dt = \hat{\mathbf{r}} \partial I / \partial t = g \nabla \phi$$
$$= k\, \partial I / \partial \phi\, \hat{\mathbf{r}} \partial \phi / \partial r$$

so

$$\partial I / \partial t = k\, \partial I / \partial r$$

i.e.

$$dr = k.dt$$

which integrates to

$$r = k.t$$

Thus we find the time t must be proportional to the radius r to satisfy our scaling requirements. This makes little sense as it stands physically, but it connects with an idea that first arose in connection with light, namely, that time is the reciprocal of radial turn. Noting that $r \propto 1/\tau$ the above result then takes the form

$$t \propto 1/\tau$$

i.e. our interpretation of potential and force in connection with gravity requires that time be inversely proportional to radial turn. There is of course a difference between requiring a mathematical relationship and making a qualitative identification, but we do now definitely propose that

the reciprocal of radial turn measures time.

By radial we mean the turn of a plane in from Ω, or more generally the turn of a plane wrt the origin plane of counterspace if that does not coincide with Ω. When it does then we have the simple picture of these planes as being tangential to equipotential spheres which are the 'level planes' for the potential, for all tangents to a sphere have the same turn in from Ω which is the polar radius of the sphere.

Eventually we may need to develop the scaling factor g, a tensor that is an invariant in polar co-ordinates, to handle rectangular co-ordinates. Also in either set of co-ordinates we need to handle rigid rotation.

Thus we now say that for gravity the gradient $\nabla\phi$ is related to $\nabla\sigma$ by

$$\nabla\sigma = g\nabla\phi, \text{ where } g \text{ scales impulse to shift and } \nabla\phi \text{ is radial.}$$

Some further implications of this approach are interesting:

$$\nabla\sigma = \mathrm{d}\mathbf{I}/\mathrm{d}t = \mathrm{d}\mathbf{p}/\mathrm{d}t = \hat{\mathbf{r}}\,\mathrm{d}p/\mathrm{d}t = -\hat{\mathbf{r}}\,\tau^2 \mathrm{d}p/\mathrm{d}\tau = -\tau^2\nabla p$$

so that the left-hand and right-hand gradients are both radial in terms of τ and we can integrate to give

$$\sigma = -\tau^2 p$$

Now σ is essentially a turn so that we can say $\sigma \propto 1/t$. We can also regard $1/t$ as a frequency ν (with dimensions T^{-1}) which implies

$$p \propto \nu$$

a well-known result in quantum physics, i.e. that frequency is proportional to the magnitude of the momentum, specifically $p = h\nu/c$. Thus our proposed relation between time and turn continues to make sense. This will need further elaboration when we look at quantum physics, to see when we may be justified in regarding τ as measuring a frequency.

In summary, we have proposed that

Stress is proportional to gradient of strain for constant temperature
Force is a counterspace vector which is a gradient

and for intensive linkages that

Stress $= \nabla\sigma = \mathbf{J}\nabla\phi$ where $\mathbf{J}$ is the Jacobian tensor for which the components $\partial x^i/\partial \xi^j$ are functions of temperature

and for extensive linkages and translations that

Potential is an actual strain between space and counterspace which is proportional to the potential impulse or momentum
Shift measures, or is scaled to, the magnitude of impulse
$\nabla\sigma = g\nabla\phi$ where g scales strain to impulse and $\nabla\phi$ is radial
Time is inversely proportional to radial turn

12. HEAT

In analysing gases and liquids we proposed that temperature affects the scaling of space and CS as expressed by $\mathbf{J}$, and saw that for gases this enables us to derive the ideal gas law as then the stress arising from the strain depends upon temperature. But the transition from geometry to physics implied does not seem to be well reflected merely by a scaling factor which is after all essentially geometric. As heat can, among other things, act as such a fundamental motive force, we expect it itself to entail stress. This is readily appreciated when we recall the intensive nature of the linkage between space and CS that we employed for gases, as the scaling can vary from CSI to CSI so that a *scaling strain* may be expected to arise if the CSIs belong to the same population, i.e. are images of the same primal CS. Clearly this has a stochastic quality since the scalings for different CSIs need not be correlated. We propose that temperature is proportional to the magnitude of the mean resulting stress and heat is the total energy content of the scaling stress. Should the scaling become uniform then we would have absolute zero as there would be no scaling stress. By scaling strain we mean that the relation of space to the primal CS appears to be different for different CSIs. This will result in stress when transformations occur, as the rates of change will be affected.

Another illustration of the idea that temperature and heat relate to scaling lies in the phenomenon of expansion which occurs when a body is heated. Such a transformation is non–metric in the sense that the volume and other metric quantities change: it is an affine transformation. Hence we conclude that after the heating the scaling between space and CS in the body must have changed. This also illustrates the idea that the scaling is not global but local, as evidently the heating of one body does not also result in the expansion of all others in the universe!

We need to consider thermal expansion, the conduction of heat, specific heat capacity, and eventually find out how to interpret the assumptions lying behind thermodynamics.

Thermal Expansion

Thermal expansion results from a change in the local scaling as we have seen. We have expressed the scaling by the tensor $\mathbf{J} = \partial x^i / \partial \xi^j$, which relates distance to turn. This suggests that the size and shape of a body are determined by planes, which seems more satisfactory from a holistic perspective. For gases we considered affine strain for linked points, and we need to relate this to **J**. In Chapter 7 we used **J** to relate stress to strain as follows:

$$\nabla\sigma = \mathbf{J}\nabla\phi$$

where $\nabla\phi$ is the strain gradient and $\nabla\sigma$ the stress gradient. Now $\nabla\sigma$ is a planewise vector in CS, so **J** transforms a pointwise vector in space to a planewise one in CS, which is what we require. The magnitude of $\nabla\sigma$ depends upon **J**, so we assume the temperature T somehow affects the magnitude of **J**. For gases and liquids both the purely expansive aspect of the scaling controlled by the leading diagonal of **J** and the rotary aspects involving viscosity controlled by the other terms are affected by T. Thus we assume that all terms $\partial x^i/\partial\xi^j$ of **J** are affected. If we denote the vector $\nabla\sigma$ by **s**, $\nabla\phi$ by **f** and let $\partial x^i/\partial\xi^j = k^i{}_j T$ then

$$s^i = f^j \partial x^i/\partial\xi^j = f^j k^i{}_j T$$

and thus if each term of **J** is proportional to T then so is each component s^i of **s**. Thus the simplest approach to the scaling gives us what we need. The determinant $|\mathbf{J}|$ is then proportional to the cube of temperature.

Thus for thermal expansion we use this fact, as **J** controls the non-translatory scaling. The coefficient of expansion α controls the change in linear size for unit temperature change, while the coefficient of cubic expansion β for volume is conventionally taken as approximately 3α if second and higher order terms in T are neglected. In the present treatment it is simpler not to ignore these terms; indeed it may be wrong (see Ref. 41 for a discussion of this).

If $\partial x^i/\partial\xi^j = k^i{}_j T$ then $\Delta x = k^i{}_j T \Delta\xi$ for small changes, so an increase in ξ (turn) results in an increase in x for constant T. An increase in turn means that the linked planes involved move towards the CSI while an increase in x means the points of the object move away from it. Strain will arise if the two aspects are not consistent, so that at some particular temperature the size of the object is such that the strain is zero, giving zero stress. This explains in holistic terms why a solid object has a definite size. Since $x \propto T$ and $\xi \propto 1/T$ an increase in temperature requires x to increase and ξ to decrease. But a decrease in turn ξ implies the corresponding plane moves away fom the CSI, so x and ξ can change with temperature such that no strain arises, i.e. incident points and planes remain in incidence. It is possible that the values of $k^i{}_j$ do not permit this, in which case there will be at most one temperature at which the strain is zero for a linear relation between **J** and T. For liquids we expect $k^i{}_j$ to be such that there is no strain so that equilibrium is maintained, but for gases $k^i{}_j$ could be such that the equilibrium point is at a high temperature so that the gas tries to expand towards it.

Latent Heat

The above considerations suggest that a large change may occur in the temperature at which a body or mass is in geometric-equilibrium, which seems a good approach to latent heat. The possibility that the strain remains zero as temperature changes seems to characterize the quality of the liquid state rather well, whereas the existence of just one strain-free temperature seems better to fit the concept of a solid, which can sustain internal stress. Then the change from one to the other would represent melting or solidification. Latent heat, which is *evolved* on solidification, would then endow the liquid with its range of strain-free temperatures, and melting would occur when the strain in the solid was so great that it could no longer be sustained. Latent heat of evaporation would then be required when a liquid could no longer sustain strain-free expansion, noting that unlike a solid a liquid is difficult to stress internally (i.e. in contrast to an external stress such as that applied by a piston). This suggests that for a solid the strain-free temperature is low, but for a gas is high or non-existent. As we saw in Chapter 8 these changes coincide with changes from metric to special-affine to purely affine linkages, so a greater energy is involved in an affine than in a metric linkage. The question remains, what form does it take? What in any case is 'energy' in the present context? In Chapter 9 the concept of affine fluidity was referred to, and some kind of internal transformations may represent that, latent heat then endowing an increased freedom of transformation. Thus we see heat as some form of internal or intensive motion, but we contrast the idea of intensive motion with that envisaged by the kinetic theory which is really scaled-down extensive motion.

Specific Heat Capacity

Specific heat capacity is defined as the heat required to raise the temperature of 1 kg by $1°K$ (in SI units), or to raise one mole by $1°K$ for a gas where there is a distinction between specific heat capacity at constant pressure and at constant volume. For us it is the heat required to change the scaling accordingly. This will be expressed mathematically in the expressions for the components $\partial x^i / \partial \xi^j$ of $\mathbf{J}$, as the factors multiplying the temperature. Qualitatively it is the corresponding change in the CSIs forming a substance, and we are led to consider the nature of that change. We expect it to be a change in the intensive motion postulated above, and thus both latent heat and specific heat capacity lead to the same question as to the nature of intensive motion. The conduction of heat too will relate to that question.

Intensive Motion

The notion of affine fluidity arose when contrasting the fractal view of gases we are postulating with the atomic theory. For an affine linkage shape is not invariant, so that an ellipsoid for example cannot be characterized further, e.g. as a sphere or species of spheroid. The fact that it can be any form that does not intersect the plane at infinity can be seen as an inherent mobility which makes it 'fluid' and seems to express the idea of affine fluidity more clearly. However, a CSI of a gas must then have some structure which can exhibit this fluidity or intensive motion. Now **J** can be represented by a quadric wrt which the polarity transformation from space to CS that it implies takes place. We will see in Chapter 14 that there is such a quadric, namely, the gauge strain threshold (GST) at which the scaling changes abruptly. Furthermore there is a kind of intensive motion within this in the sense that the scaling changes with time inside the GST after an interaction. The spatial size of this quadric depends upon the temperature, but its shape will be fluid in the above described manner for an affine linkage. For a given population of CSIs (i.e. images of the same primal CS) this motion or change in scaling will lead to strain if it is not synchronized throughout, and we can envisage the resulting stress as *heat*. Its stochastic quality will then relate to thermodynamics.

In Chapters 15 and 16 the orientation of a linkage is introduced, so that a 'spin' may be involved which could lend a vortex-like aspect to the intensive motion (albeit of a complicated kind, spiralling in from a quadric surface towards the CSI), in line with Steiner's hint in that direction in Ref. 35.

Conduction of Heat

Imbalances in the magnitude of the intensive motion and the local scaling will tend to equalize via the primal CS, i.e. heat conduction will be a fractal process rather than being mediated by impacts as in the kinetic theory. Hence the temperature will tend to equalize across a body. This may throw light on Steiner's report that heat conduction occurs in a different manner from that normally considered (Ref. 35). Now although a fractal effect of one CSI upon another is essentially instantaneous (via a primal counter-space), the relation we have proposed between time and reciprocal turn will reflect back into space as a time interval depending upon the separation of the CSIs. Thus in space conduction will appear to propagate from one CSI to the next as these time intervals are shortest for 'neighbours', although in fact the conduction does not occur that way. This turns out to be essentially the same as Steiner's description (op. cit.). At the boundary of an object there is generally a sharp discontinuity in scaling which alters or interrupts the process, suggesting that the fractal process is related to the structure of an object.

Thermodynamics

The relation between heat and time that is implied in the above discussion (as the change of scaling inside the GST concerns time) is interesting in view of the relation of heat to entropy and non-reversibility in time, essential to thermodynamics.

Warmth Ether

We pointed out in Chapter 8 that it is not correct simply to relate heat to a projective linkage. In Chapter 15 we will come closer to an understanding of what characterizes an 'ether', which involves a mode of time invariance. For heat this appears to concern how time relates to an object, as indicated at the end of the discussion of conduction. The obvious invariance is the phenomenon that the temperature across a body tends towards equilibrium, which in turn indicates that the time-invariance is that between the intensive motions within GSTs since the outer scaling may differ between substances even though they are at the same temperature.

Conclusion

This chapter suffers from the fact that a coherent treatment of heat turns out to depend upon several other aspects of the work which are incomplete. It was finished last, which accounts for the need for so many forward references. The essential idea that temperature relates to scaling arose early in the work, but that strain due to stochastic variations in scaling relates to heat is a late addition ripe for further investigation.

13. LIGHT

Light has posed tremendous challenges to modern physics. Is it intrinsically a wave or a stream of particles? Or neither? Sir Isaac Newton explored the theory that it is corpuscular so that 'rays of light' are the paths of tiny particles. It is plausible that their motion might be affected by the density of the substances they pass through, giving rise to refraction and the action of lenses. But experiments giving rise to interference phenomena such as Newton's rings and the beautiful colours produced by thin films suggested to Hooke that it is more likely to be some kind of wave. Huygens applied this idea successfully to explain refraction and reflection. Roemer explained certain apparent irregularities in the orbital periods of the moons of Jupiter by proposing that light has a finite velocity. The experiment of Michelson and Morley is currently interpreted as meaning that light has a constant velocity *in vacuo* irrespective of the motion of the observer. Planck reluctantly proposed that energy is emitted in quanta to explain why emission spectra do not conform with the classical wave theory, and Einstein gained a Nobel prize for going a step further and assuming that light is inherently quantized to explain the photoelectric effect. This is because *absorbed* light also seems to be quantized in special experimental circumstances. The uneasy marriage between a quantized particulate model and the wavelike behaviour of light has stalked physics for the whole of this century. The notion of a wave-packet arose which de Broglie then applied to particles such as electrons. By the early 1930s the puzzles posed by quantum theory led to the formulation of the Copenhagen Interpretation of quantum physics which in simple terms says that it cannot *explain* phenomena, it can only predict the probabilities with which the possible outcomes of experiments may occur. Thus naïve pictures of how, for example, single photons behave when passing through a double slit are not to be expected (in the single-photon version of Young's double-slit experiment first carried out by Taylor in 1908). More recent multiple-path experiments with single photons, in which a semi-silvered mirror offers two possible paths, show that the outcome depends upon what is placed in the two paths, as though the photon 'knows' in advance what it *might* encounter!

Meanwhile Einstein proposed that in four-dimensional space-time light travels on null-geodesics, an essentially corpuscular view. Relativity theory requires that time be treated as a dimension which has imaginary co-ordinates, in which case the length of path travelled can be zero unlike in three-dimensional Euclidean space—the shortest paths being geodesics—

so that very special geodesics can exist with zero length. Relativity mainly concerns the idea that the laws of nature are independent of the position and state of motion of the observer, but the constancy of velocity of light is basic to it. Experiments with the entangled states of photon pairs (Alain Aspect's experiment) show that if the state of polarization of one photon is determined then that of the other (distant) photon becomes instantaneously determined, apparently in defiance of Relativity. No signal should travel faster than light, and a work-around explanation is to show that no *information* can be passed faster than light by this means. The holistic qualities of the situation are undeniable and surely significant. The dual and holistic properties of projective geometry seem well suited to approach such things, in particular the notion of polar affine space.

We proposed in Chapter 8 that light is related to an affine linkage between space and counterspace for planes. The only invariants available are division ratios of lengths, areas and volumes in space and turns, polar areas and polar volumes in counterspace. We need to consider what the fundamental element or unit of linkage is for light, which must have a suitable tensor property so that we are not dependent on the co-ordinates used. For an affine or polar affine linkage between the spaces we can only seek that in one direction at a time as ratios of lengths or areas in different directions are not invariant. This is suggestive as light seems to have such a quality, for there seems to be no interaction between light propagating in different directions; light beams do not affect each other when they cross. Only when they are incident at the same location on matter does any interaction occur. Thus polar volume seems inappropriate and we must look at either turn or polar area. Rudolf Steiner found in his spiritual research that ether is essentially two dimensional, and this originally prompted the idea that we consider polar area rather than turn, i.e. that the basic invariance we examine is division ratio of polar area in one counterspace direction.

A suitable tensor is the bivector which has an interesting relationship to area. Struik (Ref. 38) explains clearly the four types of vector in affine space:

contravariant vectors represented by inner-oriented arrows
covariant vectors represented by outer-oriented areas
contravariant bivectors represented by inner-oriented areas
covariant bivectors represented by outer-oriented lines or cylinders

This may be shown diagramatically thus:

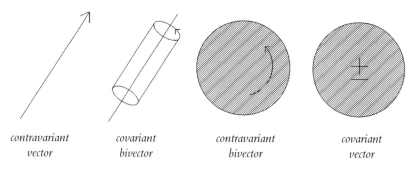

| contravariant | covariant | contravariant | covariant |
| vector | bivector | bivector | vector |

Fig. 41

For counterspace we dualize this so that instead of circles we have cones and instead of arrows we have turns between planes, as shown in Fig. 42:

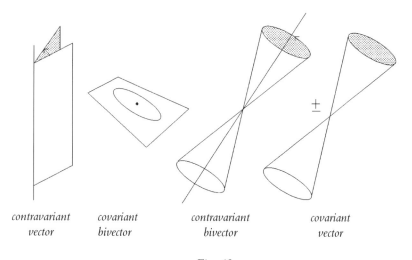

| contravariant | covariant | contravariant | covariant |
| vector | bivector | bivector | vector |

Fig. 42

A bivector is distinct from a vector in affine geometry, but in three dimensions it happens to have three components and in Euclidean metric geometry is indistinguishable from a vector. It arises as the outer product of two vectors, which in two dimensions has only one component but in four dimensions has six, showing clearly its distinctness from vectors.

The polar area of a cone consists of all the planes through its vertex that do not intersect it, and is evaluated by integrating over those planes wrt turn. The result as we saw in Chapter 3 is $\pi\rho^2$ where ρ is its polar radius. A further important result is that for a given scaling—and working in metric

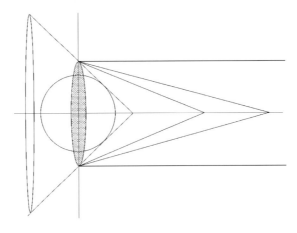

Fig. 43

space—the product of its polar area and the area of the circle in which a cone intersects the plane through the CSI orthogonal to its axis is constant (see Fig. 43).

The area of the circle is shown shaded and various cones are shown containing it. All these cones have the same polar area, including the cylinder which has its vertex at infinity. However, their polar areas are only comparable in metric counterspace. To be comparable in polar-affine space two cones must share the same vertex, which is the dual of two circles in the same plane. This will be important for interference and absorption. The above diagram will relate to emission which is initially a metric process.

We now propose that the fundamental linkage between space and counterspace for light is a contravariant bivector in counterspace. This can as well be thought of as a cylinder as a cone, and since it must also manifest in space the most suitable tensor is a covariant bivector, which is also representable by a cylinder. The principal reason for choosing a contravariant bivector rather than a covariant vector, which is also a cone, is that the former has an inner orientation or sense of rotation that may be related to polarization and spin.

We now complete this idea by postulating that

a photon is a linkage between space and counterspace which is a contravariant bivector in counterspace and a covariant bivector in space.

We will refer to these entities as *photon cones or photon cylinders*. In quantum physics a photon quantum state is uniquely defined by specifying its

energy
polarization
direction of motion

A photon cylinder has the following three properties:

polar area in the metric case
a sense of rotation
a direction

The photon cylinder has two modes of directionality as it is a linkage: along a line in space and wrt a point in counterspace, for division ratios of a covariant bivector must be taken about a line in space, and about a point for a contravariant bivector in counterspace.

It can plausibly be argued (Ref. 13) that the circular polarization states of photons can be regarded as the most natural choice of polarization state, and other polarization states are superpositions of these. This question arises when discussing the quantization of angular momentum.

Thus at first glance the photon cylinder seems to reflect the properties experiment requires of conventional photons, if polar area is related to energy and thus in some way to colour. It is too simplistic to identify colour either with energy or polar area, but we must postpone further discussion of this for now. We may thus regard the photon cylinder as defining an ensemble of photon cones all having the same polar area as that cylinder (when an interaction occurs to render the photon metric). The cones are all polar-parallel as their areas are calculated wrt to polar-parallel points (lying on the axis of the cylinder which contains the CSI).

After emission a photon cone may be imagined to become a cylinder, in which case it will be a very thin cylinder, the light itself being in the polar area all round the cylinder, so that the cylinder itself amounts to a *ray of darkness*. This can explain why the ray model for light works when applied to lenses, mirrors, prisms etc. as long as it is recalled that the rays are not actually rays of light.

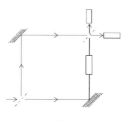

Fig. 44

If we consider a typical beam-splitter experiment (Fig. 44) we begin to see the explanatory possibilities of this approach to photons.

An incident photon is shown by the arrow approaching the lower semi-silvered mirror represented by the dashed line. Two possible paths for the photon are shown via mirrors ending at another semi-silvered mirror and two detectors. In one path an object is shown which may block the photon. Experiments indicate that the photon behaves as though it 'knows' in advance whether one path is blocked or not, because if it is unblocked only one detector responds with a probability of 1, but if the obstruction is present then both detectors may respond with a probability of 0.5 after many repeats. This curious and counter-intuitive outcome is usually difficult to comprehend fully, but if the proposed photon cylinder approach is adopted instead then the polar area is all round the 'ray' and thus embraces the whole apparatus before it interacts with the semi-silvered mirror. The experimental results thus become more comprehensible in principle without needing to resort to explanations such as the many-worlds one. Of course a detailed treatment will be necessary, but this shows the promise of this approach to photons and linked light.

When a photon interacts with matter it becomes metrically related to space, and thus the bivectors may change quality since in three-dimensional Euclidean space vectors and bivectors are indistinguishable, and also the distinction between covariance and contravariance disappears. Thus the bivector may evolve in four possible ways: to remain as a contravariant bivector, to become a covariant vector, to become a contravariant vector, or to become a covariant bivector. Since these are now indistinguishable we mean that the further behaviour of the photon may reflect any one of the qualitative properties of these four types of vector, so that its orientation may act like an outer instead of an inner one, or it may lose its relation to polar area and acquire a relation to turn instead. We expect the qualities of the spatial aspect of the vector to remain consistent with that of the counterspace one, so that both vectors have the qualities either of vectors or bivectors, and they continue to act as though they have opposite variances. This is summed up in Fig. 45, where we also indicate a possible relation to the four processes of diffraction, refraction, reflection and absorption.

Diffraction and refraction are more external interactions with matter in the sense that onward transmission occurs, in which we expect the cone to remain as shown above, whereas reflection and absorption are more intimate interactions suggesting a more radical change in the vector quality. Thus refraction relates to an outer orientation of the counterspace vector and to a directional quality of the spatial aspect, absorption results in a change in angular momentum well represented by the axis and area of a spatial contravariant bivector, reflection is represented by the turn of a plane, and diffraction as the most external interaction leaves the vector qualities unchanged.

Another way of expressing this is to consider what remains invariant before and after the interaction, so that some aspect of turn remains invariant for reflection whereas polar area remains invariant for diffraction and refraction. For the spatial aspect oriented area is invariant for reflection

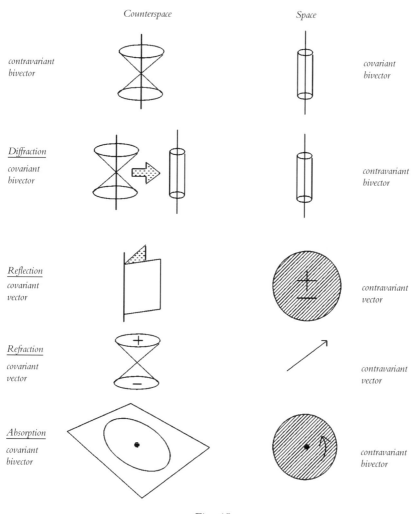

Fig. 45

and absorption, an inner orientation for absorption giving a spin axis for the angular momentum, and an outer one for reflection relating to Compton 'scattering'. The counterspace covariant bivector represented by a circle (dual to a cylinder) matches the spatial bivector, in accord with the fact that the photon is quite changed and its radiant qualities are lost on absorption.

Interactions

When a photon cone is emitted we can provisionally imagine it 'expanding' towards the form of a cylinder so that the spatial and counterspatial bivectors are then both cylinders and its spatial location becomes pointwise indeterminate. If a material object exists in its cone we assume that it interacts with it, the vertex being at the point of interaction. The reason for this is that an object within the polar area clearly does not prevent the photon from propagating, or no photons would ever be emitted! On the other hand an object in its path clearly does affect it. The multi-path experiments referred to above show, however, that the polar area relates to objects in some subtle manner. A difficulty lies in the way we tend to think about light (Ref. 43), and in particular we question here the idea that the photon travels at all, i.e. the notion that it has a velocity and moves. We will explore this in more detail below.

The reason why a material object in its path affects it is that it has a finite polar area wrt the CSI or CSIs involved which may differ from its intrinsic polar area. This is because either they are not on its axis, or their scaling tensor differs from that of the source CSI. The result is strain and stress which cause a change in the photon to minimize it. By 'lying in its path' we mean lying Euclideanly inside the cylinder. On the other hand wrt CSIs lying outside the cylinder the latter has an infinite polar area which no adjustment can correct as there are enormous amounts of matter for which this applies, and we assume that such CSIs as a rule have no effect on the photon. A single CSI in its cone may cause it to rotate so as to bring that CSI either onto its axis or outside it, which would be the basis of scattering.

Since polar area is only polar-affinely comparable at a point (dual to areas in affine space only being comparable if in the same plane) we see that we may relate the polar area at the *vertex* to that of the new post-interaction cone and thus ensure its invariance. This is the reason for assuming that the vertex must be at the point of interaction. It particularly applies to inter-actions where the photon retains its cone form and so polar area is invariant. If no change of the cone allows the polar area to be invariant then either turn or area are conserved instead and the bivector changes type.

To clarify this we show in Fig. 46 how diffraction may be approached as an example of the constant polar area type of interaction.

The top diagram shows a photon cylinder with an intruding obstruction and the most 'expanded' possible cone which excludes the object. The vertex is at P and is the interaction point for an affine comparison. Another cylinder is shown related to a new cone sharing the vertex P and such that it just clears the obstruction. The new cylinder must have the same polar area as the original (or, to be affinely strict, have a ratio to it of 1). The lower diagram shows a similar arrangement but with the obstruction closer to the axis of the cylinder so that the deviation is greater. This captures some of the essential features of diffraction: the obstruction must be suf-

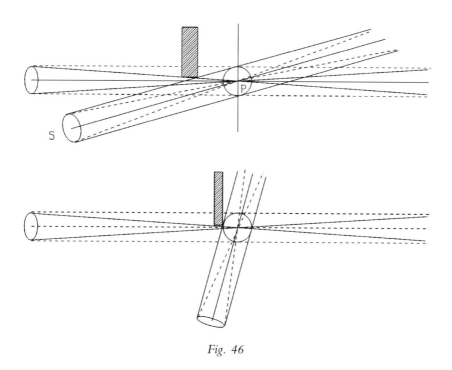

Fig. 46

ficiently close to the axis (of the same order of magnitude as a wavelength conventionally, which indicates how wavelength may be reinterpreted), and the closer it is the greater the deviation. Also, the greater the polar radius the closer the obstruction must be for the same deviation, relating to the difference caused by colour. An observer will see the diffracted photon as if it were emitted from a source S located where the new photon cone and photon cylinder intersect. We will explore this further, but for now it is merely intended to illustrate the approach being taken to interactions.

Light and Time

If a photon is emitted as shown in Fig. 47 then it interacts with anything in its cylinder. Thus if a photo-multiplier or other detector is located in the cylinder the vertex will be located on the detector at the moment of interaction. If the spatial distance of the vertex from the source is r and the turn of the plane α through the vertex (which defines the polar radius ρ) is τ, then for a given scaling $r\tau = $ constant. Now τ is a radial turn, i.e. it is the turn of α wrt the plane at infinity, since α is symmetrical such that it is the reference for ρ. In Chapter 11 we proposed that such radial turns are inversely proportional to time, so we have $r/t = $ constant. Thus no matter

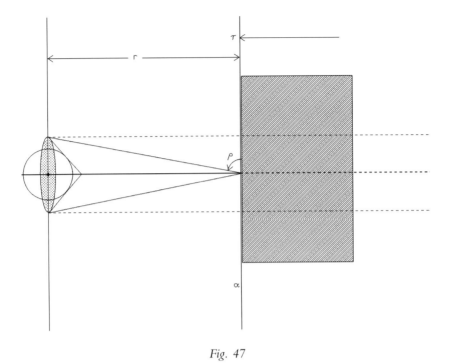

Fig. 47

where the photomultiplier is placed in the photon cylinder the ratio r/t will appear to be the same, and clearly this is unaffected by the velocity of the detector. This fact has two consequences:

1. It explains why an apparent velocity can be associated with light despite the fact that the light does not 'travel' in the way a material particle does.
2. That apparent velocity will always be judged to be the same *in vacuo* (or for the same scaling) regardless of the motion of the observer or detector. Special Relativity is required to explain this conventionally.

Thus we agree with the experimental facts supporting the constancy of 'velocity' of light, but we note that those experiments need reinterpreting to remove the idea that light travels, and to assimilate the idea that in reality no velocity is actually involved. Since radial turn measures time we cannot naïvely think of the vertex of a photon cone as travelling outwards with some velocity because we would then be assuming another measure of time. The photon cylinder defines all possible cones with the same polar area, and the one that 'actualizes' in an interaction is determined by the whole context. For example, the observations made by Roemer of the irregularities in the periods of the moons of Jupiter can be explained by the different radial turns associated with them depending upon the distance of the earth from Jupiter.

This in turn implies that there is an instantaneous relationship between a source and observer so that the light is established between the two; it is a mutual or 'two-way' affair, unlike the conventional view that something travels from the source to the observer. Time is then judged according to the radial turn involved. This may help us to understand the experiment by Alain Aspect in connection with Bell's Inequality in quantum physics, for the problem it raises is an apparent conflict with Relativity since two greatly separated photons must change their quantum state simultaneously, apparently going against 'the spirit of Relativity' as Roger Penrose expressed it when launching his book *Shadows of the Mind*. This is not a problem for our approach as Relativity is not needed to explain the behaviour of light. Steiner found that there is a mutuality in the sense that light goes out from the eye of the observer as well as entering it (Ref. 36). This was a report of his spiritual research which we can now interpret as above. However, we must extend the idea to all relationships between sources and detectors or other obstructions.

Reflection

We saw that for reflection the bivector changes to act as a contravariant vector for which turn is invariant across the reflection. We take the base plane of this vector as the plane α tangential to the surface, and relate all planes in the polar area to it. The lines of action of these vectors then lie in α, and the reflected planes forming the polar area of the emergent cone will share those lines of action and their turns will be conserved. This gives the observed reflection law as shown for two representative planes in Fig. 48.

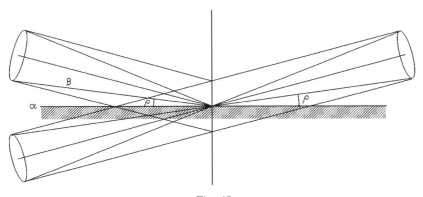

Fig. 48

The incident cone and cylinder are shown on the left above the mirror, and the turn ρ between α and the tangent plane β is shown, which is conserved through the reflection. The turn ρ of the reflected tangent plane will be measured wrt a virtual source located where the reflected cylinder and cone intersect as shown, which agrees with the usual appearance of virtual images. The polar area of the incident and reflected cones is comparable at their coincident vertices, which then gives that of the reflected cylinder. It is clear that all incident and reflected planes making up the polar areas satisfy the stated conditions if the axes of the two cones are coplanar with the normal as shown.

If the vector is regarded as that between just two planes, we would take α and the centre-plane of the incident cone (i.e. that wrt which the polar radius ρ is defined), which in metric space appears normal to the axis. The invariance of turn and line-of-action give the reflected centre-plane, and then the above treatment of the component planes of the polar area shows how the contravariant bivector is reconstituted for the reflected cone.

For curved mirrors the above considerations apply for each tangent plane, yielding the known behaviour of such mirrors without difficulty.

Refraction

Refraction is more subtle. In Chapter 11 it was pointed out that the scaling between space and counterspace depends upon the substance filling space. The scaling will thus change as the light passes from one medium to another, and it is this which causes the deviation observed as refraction. We saw earlier that the presence of CSIs relating to matter inside the cylinder causes strain as its polar area wrt them may not equal its emission polar area. An imbalance arises at a boundary as we shall now see. Figure 49 shows a photon cylinder at a boundary between two media.

Since both are transparent we show an incident photon cylinder rather than a cone which, as we proposed earlier, retains the outer orientation of its polar area invariant through the interaction. This is balanced for the main part of the cylinder, but at the interface there is an imbalance. This is shown by the lightly shaded cylindrical wedge of volume indicated, where there are more CSIs on the right than on the left for which the cylinder has a very large polar area. If the incident cylinder existed unaltered across the boundary then there would be a similar wedge above the boundary, and as the scaling has changed the two would not balance each other. If the refracted cylinder is as shown its wedge will have a different volume which may balance the incident wedge. We work with spatial volume which is easy to evaluate, recalling that the product of volume and polar volume is

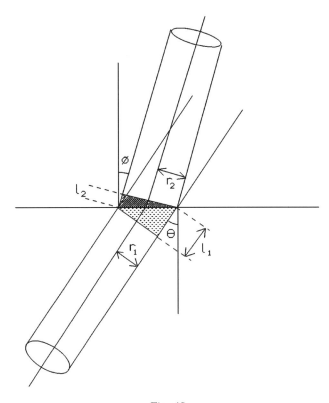

Fig. 49

constant, which justifies that. The volume of the incident wedge is

$$\frac{\pi r_1^2 l_1}{2}$$

where r_1 is the spatial radius of the incident cylinder and l_1 the length of the complete cylindrical segment of which the wedge is a half. For the refracted cylinder the volume is

$$\frac{\pi r_1 r_2 l_2}{2}$$

where r_2 is the length of the semi-major axis of the elliptic cross-section of the refracted cylinder, and l_2 its length. For evaluating polar area the scaling has changed, and we assume its ratio to that of the incident medium is $1/n$, so that the polar area A_2 is divided by n_2 and hence the spatial area $\pi r_1 r_2$ is multiplied by n^2; l_2 is also scaled by n. We require the two volumes and polar areas to be equal for the required balance, so

$$\pi r_1{}^2 l_1 = n^3 \pi r_1 r_2 l_2$$
$$= (n^2 \pi r_1 r_2) n l_2$$
$$= (\pi r_1{}^2) n l_2$$
i.e. $l_1 = n l_2$

Clearly the lengths l_1 and l_2 are proportional to the sines of the angles of incidence and refraction θ and ϕ, and we thus deduce Snell's Law that the refractive index is given by

$$n = \frac{l_1}{l_2} = \frac{\sin \theta}{\sin \phi}$$

The refractive index is thus the ratio of the scalings for the two media.

This is a simplified analysis in which we have merely balanced the polar volumes of the cylindrical wedges. That *polar* volume is what is balanced is shown by the fact that we have not related the l_i to the r_i via the tangents as would be required spatially. A deeper analysis is needed to bring out the dependence of n on the polar area, and hence to account for dispersion, which will require an integration over the wedge of the actual effect of the imbalance on the photon.

We should also note that the elliptic cross-section of the refracted cylinder need not be retained beyond the metric interaction at the boundary between the media, as once it reverts to an affine linkage again the distinction between ellipticity and circularity is lost.

An interesting question yet to be tackled is the ratio between refraction and reflection at such a boundary, where the elliptic aspect may be involved so as to account for polarization, if a subsequent interaction causes the metric situation to be sustained. In that case the polarization will be a spatial phenomenon dictated by the matter involved, but not a property of the light itself which is affine (c.f. Steiner's findings on this in Ref. 35).

Interference

Interference phenomena are conventionally explained as the result of either constructive or destructive addition of waves according to their relative phase. We will need some results from later work on chemistry and the chemical ether to work this out fully, but the main principle can be illustrated here. The diagram shows coherent light passing through two slits, and falling on a screen.

The lines coming from similar positions in the slits represent the axes of two photon cylinders, which assume the form of cones due to the interaction, with their vertices coincident on the screen. Their polar areas are

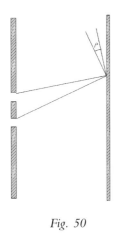

Fig. 50

then comparable. For interference to occur there must be some structure of the planes in the polar areas that controls how they are added together, so that the resultant brightness may vary from light to dark as the vertex moves vertically down the screen. None of our considerations so far can account for this as we have not yet introduced structure into the polar areas of photon cones. This consideration indicates the necessity for this, but it requires an understanding of how darkness and rhythmicity can become incorporated into light, which in turn depends upon the chemical ether. The same applies to coherence which is also important in connection with interference phenomena.

Diffraction

We considered diffraction when explaining interactions. The main features were explained, but diffraction through a narrow slit was omitted. This again depends upon the structure within a photon cone and further work on this must be postponed until that is clear. The effect of differing polar area was only briefly mentioned, and the diagram below shows this in more detail.

The top diagram of Fig. 51 shows an incident photon cylinder with a smaller polar area than that of the similar cylinder in the lower diagram, and hence with a smaller polar radius and a larger physical radius. The two obstructions are at equal distances from the axes. In accordance with the earlier indication that polar area relates to energy, we associate red with the smaller polar area and blue with the larger, and it can be seen that the red photon is diffracted more than the blue one. This is the principle of the diffraction grating which produces colours in this manner.

Polarization

This has yet to be treated in detail. An indication was given when discussing refraction that it might relate to the metric form of the cross-section of the photon cylinder, i.e. elliptic or circular.

Scattering

Scattering occurs when isolated counterspace infinities lie in a photon cone.

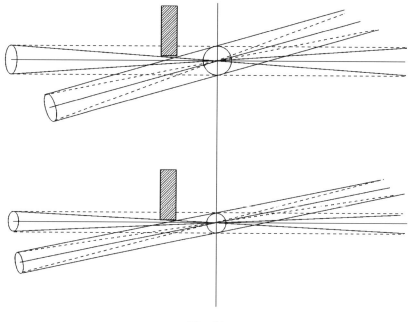

Fig. 51

The upper diagram of Fig. 52 shows a counterspace infinitude with its associated self-polar surface (SPS, dark shading, see Chapter 16) inside a photon cylinder. The most expanded possible cone is shown (lightly shaded) which does not Euclideanly contain the infinitude. The axis of the scattered cylinder is shown passing through the infinitude and the vertex of

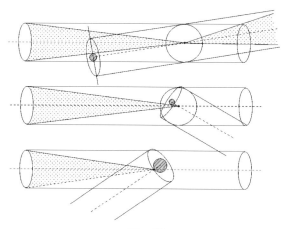

Fig. 52

that cone, and the new cylinder arises accordingly. The scattered cone is also shown lightly shaded, illustrating once again the principle of affine comparison of polar area at a point. The large circle concentric with the vertex is purely illustrative and to aid construction.

The centre picture illustrates the effect on the angle of forward scatter of the position of the infinitude wrt the axis.

The lower picture shows how back-scatter arises. We still need to see when this case may instead lead to absorption, e.g. with a large SPS. The basis for reaction cross-sections is suggestively indicated in these diagrams.

These diagrams show, to indicate the principle clearly, the unlikely case of isolated infinitudes in a photon cone, e.g. in outer space. In the atmosphere where there are many infinitudes within it we have a balanced situation as mentioned above in connection with refraction. The lower diagram is most relevant in this case since for radiation with small polar radius cylinders compared with the polar radius of the SPS the probability of this case arising is small, the cases for the upper diagrams being balanced out anyway. However the larger the polar radius the greater the probability of the case in the lower diagram arising. The situation needs a closer analysis but the basis is clear for the relation of scattering to polar radius, i.e. relatively small polar radius radiation passing easily through a medium.

Emission and the Balmer Series

Figure 53 shows a set of cones tangential to a sphere which we take to be that of a self-polar surface (see Chapter 16). It is shown in Chapter 3 that the polar area of the cones is

$$k^2 \pi \left(\frac{1}{r^2} - \frac{1}{h^2} \right)$$

where r is the radius of the sphere
           h is the distance of the vertex from the centre
           k is the scaling factor to convert distances to turns.

Thus if r is fixed and h an integral multiple of it we essentially have the formula for the Lyman, Balmer and similar series. We envisage emission to take place when a cone detaches itself from a SPS and then 'expands' with constant polar area. The reason for the integral relation between h and r is yet to be found.

Images

An important phenomenon relating to light is the formation of images. An image has a holistic quality that involves many photon cones. Since their

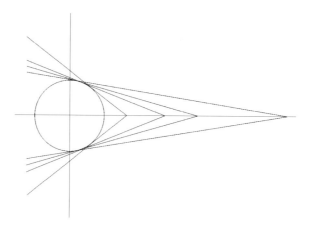

Fig. 53

polar areas are only comparable when their vertices coincide we see why points are important, e.g. a pinhole camera, and why images are so often handled conventionally by considering rays in points. The counterspace view is not that, but once again we find the reason why a conventional approach works as a model. A special case is when the common vertex lies in the plane at infinity giving a parallel beam of photon cylinders.

Colour

We do not intend to treat colour here, but the association of polar area with colour above requires some comment. Colour is much more complicated than the simple correspondence with energy or polar area suggests. Its dependence upon context is notorious and is usually explained away as being subjective. However that ignores the obvious fact that colour is qualitatively different from any quantitative property, and the relation of colour to wavelength for example is purely empirical and is in any case itself dependent upon the observer and the context. To say that cadmium green 'is' radiation with a wavelength of 5.08582×10^{-7} m is naïve in the extreme as 'green' is one experience and the measurement of that radiation is quite another. That different photon energies or polar areas have a relation to the conditions under which certain colours may be experienced is clearly the case, but a simple identification is out of the question both philosophically and scientifically. Heisenberg acknowledged this distinction when discussing Goethe's theory of colour (Ref. 18), although he judged Newton's to be superior. What remains of great interest is to see how colour as such relates to, or manifests in, particular quantitative situations.

14. TIME

The interpretation of radial turn as the reciprocal of time has various implications. To start with we do not envisage absolute time but rather time intervals. Thus the radial turn between two Euclideanly parallel planes with turns τ_1 and τ_2 wrt Ω represents a time interval given by

$$\delta t = \frac{1}{\tau_1} - \frac{1}{\tau_2} = k(r_1 - r_2) = \frac{\delta r}{c}$$

assuming c is the scaling constant *in vacuo*. We assume for now that the plane at infinity Ω is the zero-plane for counterspace wrt which radial turns are calculated. This need not be the case depending upon the way space and counterspace are linked.

If we are concerned with actions within a sphere (Euclideanly speaking) then δr has an upper limit and hence so does δt. Thus for events within very small spheres only very short time intervals are possible, and a slow change must then be quantized in a 'stop/start' fashion into a series of changes requiring time intervals $\leq \delta r/c$, with intervening intervals of inaction. This shows why very short time intervals are significant for actions on an atomic scale.

For an affine linkage time intervals are not comparable in different directions. If the scaling *in vacuo* is constant for all directions then we can explain why the behaviour of light in one direction is consistent with that in another provided there is a linkage. The relation of Ω to direction is interesting in this respect, for it is parallel to every plane in space and thus provides a reference that overcomes the affine problem. For unlinked, purely etheric light this is not the case and other laws apply.

Otherwise turns do not represent time intervals. Tangent planes to a sphere—which all have the same radial separation from Ω—are all separated by zero time intervals, and turns relative to such planes have a zero radial component if the line of action touches the sphere. If Ω is not the zero-plane of counterspace for a linkage then a counterspace sphere appears in space as a prolate spheroid with the CSI at a focus and the zero-plane ω as its polar plane. This is proved in Appendix 6. This raises interesting questions about the way such a linkage relates timewise to other linkages, for it has a different zero-reference from linkages with Ω for their zero-plane. Thus there will be a possible conflict of the sign of time intervals if they are related in the opposite sense to the zero-planes.

This leads into the question of strain related to time, for two CSIs belonging to the same population and with the same scaling will see the

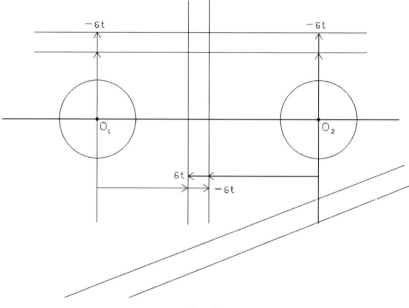

Fig. 54

radial turn between two planes orthogonal, say, to the line O_1O_2 as of opposite sign if between them (Fig. 54).

On the other hand planes parallel to O_1O_2, or else not separating the CSIs, suffer no such turn strain and hence no time discrepancy. The region over which this strain exists is reduced if the separation between the CSIs decreases, so we expect some attractive force to arise in order to reduce the strain. An example of this situation arises if there is a linked cone related to the two CSIs and such that some of the planes forming the polar area intersect O_1O_2 between them (Fig. 55).

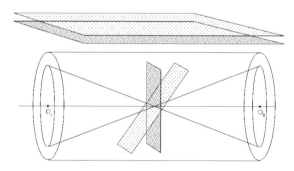

Fig. 55

Extreme cases are on the one hand photon cones co-axial with O_1O_2 and with their vertices between O_1 and O_2 as all the planes in the polar area suffer this kind of strain, and on the other hand co-axial photon cylinders for which there is no strain. Thus the first kind of photon cone will lead to attraction. If the CSIs are constrained not to move then we may expect the effect to react back on the photon, tending to align its axis parallel to O_1O_2 so as to remove the strain. The magnitude of the effect may be expected to depend upon the distance of the axis of the photon from the CSIs, and this may account for the bending of light observed near massive objects which is otherwise predicted by General Relativity.

Since the polar area of the cone with its vertex between O_1 and O_2 is equal wrt both CSIs when the vertex is equidistant between them, we see that it will be trapped by them, which may relate to bonding and absorption. Otherwise polar-area strain will arise.

Another aspect of turn strain with an implication for time is that a linked plane may appear to have a different radial turn wrt to two fractally related CSIs if it is not parallel to their common line (see Fig. 56).

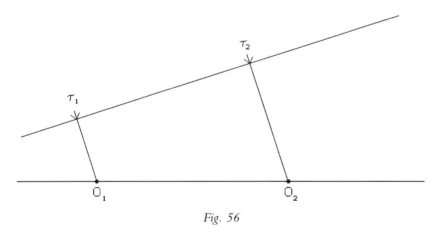

Fig. 56

Thus the turn strain is $\tau_1 - \tau_2$, but it now relates to a single plane. The cover of the book shows the pattern of planes suffering equal strain. This implies a time discrepancy that has opposite senses as seen by the two CSIs, and in view of this ambiguity in sign we propose that it is expressed as a *frequency* ν given by the reciprocal of the time difference. This implies an interpretation of wavelength λ as being equal to the radial discrepancy δr, which then agrees with the usual relation $c = \lambda\nu$. However we do not have a wave here, unless it is a standing wave. This has particular relevance to the captured photon cone described above since all its planes will be associated with frequencies in this way, forming a wide spectrum. However it is reasonable to suppose that it does not have such a wide spectrum if polar area is indeed related to colour as indicated in Chapter 13, so we might expect the linked planes within its polar area to be restricted to a set all having the same frequency, i.e. to a set of tangents to a cone, presumably the tangents of the photon cone itself which involve the least strain since δr is smallest for them. This brings structure into the polar area, which we anticipated earlier should arise. For a cone with its vertex on the line O_1O_2 the discrepancy in time is *only* one of sign, which is more subtle. There are mathematical entities which possess an inherent sign ambiguity, namely, spinors, so when a photon is trapped in this way spinors may play a role.

Another source of strain arises due to the turn between any two planes of a photon cone appearing to be different as seen by the two CSIs. Such a turn also resolves into radial and tangential components in different ways wrt to the two CSIs (c.f. Appendix 3 for the way vectors are resolved in counterspace). Thus it has conflicting relationships to time as well as to tangential turn. Is there a way of eliminating or minimizing this? One way is for the cone to evolve into a photon cylinder, and this provides a cogent reason why an emitted photon cone will either rapidly or instantaneously evolve into a cylinder. Another way is for the polar area to collapse as before into the tangent planes of the cone, which eliminates tangential strain but leaves strain in the form of frequency. We conclude that the polar area of a photon cone 'contracts'—when closely related to two CSIs—into the tangent planes of the cone, which eliminates time and tangential strain but leaves frequency.

We now see that frequency only arises when light is intimately related to matter or 'darkness'. Such a contraction removes the 'light' of the photon cone as the polar area has been 'emptied out', and so a cone acting as a bond (as suggested above) is no longer 'light'. We begin to approach what might underlie the conventional view that the electromagnetic force is mediated by photons if the bond we looked at earlier relates to charge in some way. Steiner referred to electricity as 'fallen light' (Ref. 33), which our considerations begin to approach since the light *has* fallen in a way, from a complete filling of the polar area to a frequency-based set of tangent planes. This would interpret Steiner's finding as relating to the active or bonding aspect of electricity rather than the static view of it as charge.

Some quantitative relationship between frequency and polar area is implied by all this. Certainly the greater the polar area the greater the polar radius and hence the less the turn strain of tangent planes, which in turn implies δt is smaller and hence the frequency is greater.

We recall that momentum requires time to be the reciprocal of radial turn, so if there *is* no radial component of turn then there may be no momentum either. The above considerations also serve to show why frequency may be associated with momentum. Then momentum will only come to be associated with photons when they interact with CSIs and acquire radial components of turn between the planes of their polar areas. If related to a heterogeneous collection of CSIs there is little chance of this being eliminated, but if a bound photon can relate to a structure of CSIs such that it has no radial turn components wrt that structure it will have no momentum and we may begin to approach phenomena such as super-conductivity. This would imply that electrical resistance entails momentum which restricts and hampers the movement of bound photons. Regarding the conservation of momentum, this is only measurable by the effect of light on matter, and all such measurements entail the fall of light as described, with the attendant engendering of momentum. That momentum is gained and lost with the absorption and emission of photons, as sensitive measurements indicate, does not in fact prove that photons have intrinsic momentum, only that interactions always entail it in such a way that they can be interpreted as though there was a conservation.

We have not yet considered absolute time. Because $\delta t \propto \delta r$ a moving plane traverses the same time interval for a given step wrt all CSIs and thus time intervals are globally consistent. However we saw earlier that there is a conflict of sign even if not of magnitude when that plane separates two CSIs. This requires linked planes to remain motionless if all conflict is to be avoided, and in the case of light that is accomplished by the photon cones becoming cylinders so that there is no motion of their constituent planes. If a linked plane moves then the issue of time strain arises, and such an action will then involve some kind of stress which must be overcome, suggesting that work is done.

An important question to be resolved is how absolute time relates to interactions. If time increases radially outwards in counterspace, then a given linked plane would have a time co-ordinate of $1/\tau$ at the moment of interaction, after which this must increase for time to elapse. This is difficult to envisage consistently for all CSIs, and an alternative is that a CSI 'retreats inwards' after an interaction has occurred. Thus at the moment of an interaction the location of a CSI in space may be precise, but that precision may be lost as time elapses. This is an aspect of the 'fluidity' of an assemblage of CSIs such as a gas. What the nature of the appearance of a CSI is after time has elapsed is an interesting question. We are reminded of the re-emergence of the wave function after it has 'collapsed' due to an interaction. The ideas to be presented later on the chemical ether relate to surfaces containing standing waves, so this opens up an interesting possible reinterpretation of that collapse, and of its aftermath. The topology of this idea presents challenges.

In Chapter 16 we define a self-polar quadric surface (SPS) round a CSI as part of its structure. One way of thinking about the 'retreat inwards' is to regard the SPS related to a CSI as being of a fixed size in space, in which case the scaling will have to change with time. This is clearly rather difficult to accommodate unless we postulate different scalings inside and outside the SPS, so that outside it (Euclideanly speaking) the scaling is constant to allow refraction and so forth to remain consistent, while inside it the scaling is changing as the CSI 'retreats inwards'. Thus the time interval between Ω and a tangent plane to the SPS is constant, as it is for any plane that does not intersect the surface, but is changing for any plane that intersects the SPS. This leads us to refer to the SPS as the *gauge strain threshold* (GST) as there is a scaling discontinuity at that surface.

It follows that spatial assemblages of CSIs will tend to be such that no linked planes intersect their SPSs. This may have a bearing on crystal structure with its planar properties, rigidity and the astonishingly accurate flatness of the faces (by contrast, how accurate is the orientation of a conventionally conceived bond to enable the atoms to produce such flatness non-holistically?).

These ideas also suggest a link with cosmological ideas where the Hubble constant relates radial distance with time for an expanding universe, and black holes are supposed to involve a 'retreat inwards' as they collapse. The hypothetical event horizon is like our SPS, involving as it does a discontinuity, and a different relation to time inside and outside that horizon. Such ideas seem to mirror in an extensively conceived manner the intensive properties of a counterspace. Is this their true significance?

If we have nested surfaces then there will be a stable temporal region between the surfaces, and the 'retreat' will occur within the innermost one. This opens up the possibility of a time structure for a counterspace. Furthermore when another interaction occurs this time structure must 'collapse', suggesting that the conventional wave function is related to it. It would seem reasonable to postulate that in such a case the scaling inside the GST becomes continuous with that outside it, which captures the idea that measurements and interactions involve a realignment with the macroscopic world, which could correspond to the 'R' function (state vector reduction) discussed by Penrose ('the basic X-mystery of quantum physics', see Ref. 25).

Two spatially separated GSTs cannot approach too closely without a change of signature of their surfaces, for each appears as a hyperboloid wrt the other in counterspace, and this changes to an ellipsoid if the CSI of one crosses the surface of the other. Such a transformation is radical and would require the linkage to revert to a purely projective one as even in affine geometry the signature is conserved. This may explain why matter does not collapse. Conversely if two CSIs are each inside the GST of the other then a strong force is required to separate them as again a signature change is involved. The range is about right to explain the strong force in physics, which comes into play very abruptly at close ranges.

Another interesting aspect of this approach to time is the possibility that the structure of a primal counterspace evolves with time. This might be expected as within it time increases radially outwards, so that past inter-actions or events may leave some kind of record. If that aspect of the structure can influence further interactions then we make contact with Rupert Sheldrake's hypothesis (Ref. 45) that the past can influence the present. Of course we will need to find out how resistant a counterspace is to such changes, as too great a sensitivity would lead to instability.

We are left with the need for two scaling tensors instead of just one ($\mathbf{J}$), one for the outside and the other for the inside of the GST. It shows that for nuclear physics a different scaling and different laws will apply. This is yet to be explored.

15. ETHERS AND CHEMISTRY

We have seen that the radial dimension of counterspace is related to time. Steiner's research indicated that the ethers are two-dimensional (Ref. 32), and we now propose that the remaining two-dimensionality of counterspace apart from the radial concerns the ether. More specifically we consider the possible time–invariant transformations of counterspace as relating to the ethers. We have seen one example developed in some detail for light. In that case polar area was invariant wrt time, which somewhat paradoxically exhibited how radial transformations can be set in a time invariant context.

Another possibility is to consider transformations in the surface of a sphere in counterspace, which will also be time invariant since its tangent planes all have the same turn wrt Ω. However in the affine case we cannot compare turns in different directions and thus we cannot take an arbitrary rotation as being time invariant, for example. We must instead consider local turns in the surface which are purely tangential, i.e. which have no radial component. It is shown in Appendix 3 how to resolve counterspace vectors, and in particular we see there that the lines of action of vectors with no radial component are tangential to the sphere. Thus we are concerned with vectors at tangent planes with their lines of action as indicated. We are using the term 'sphere' to refer to any central quadric enclosing O, as in affine geometry they are indistinguishable. We are now concerned with the transformations which leave the sphere invariant, and all turns in its surface must remain tangential. Any two tangent planes may be regarded as defining a vector, which has both a radial and a tangential component. A transformation that leaves the radial component invariant must transform the vector into one with its radial component in the same counterspace direction as that of the original so that those components may be compared. Now two lines of action are in the same direction in counterspace if they lie in a plane containing O. Radial vectors have their lines of action in Ω, so to meet this condition the two vectors must have identical lines of action in Ω as there is only one plane through O and a line in Ω, i.e. the base planes must be parallel, as is obvious intuitively.

Figure 57 shows a vector consisting of the two tangent planes A, B intersecting in the plane η, and its radial component AC is constructed taking A as the base plane. There are three other vectors shown with the same radial component, i.e. with affinely equal radial components: AD, EF and EH. Clearly the identity transformation and a rotation through $180°$ meet our requirements for all such vectors, the latter being an affine

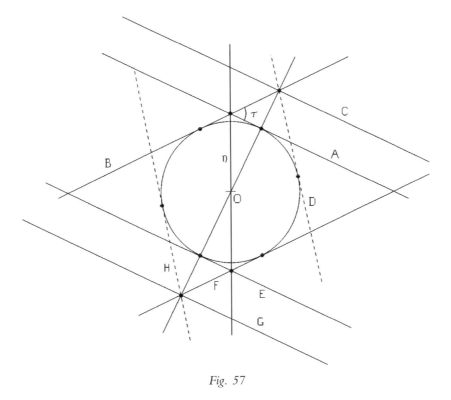

Fig. 57

rotation such that all planes through O transform into themselves (so that the case is met for ellipsoids in general). Although reflections are affine transformations, they do not permit the comparison of turns we require for all surface vectors. Thus apart from the identity we see that the only transformation that is time invariant for all tangent-plane vectors is a plastic rotation through $180°$. This gives but one solution, which is linear.

If instead we have a situation where only a finite number of tangent planes are linked then other rotations are possible. Considering planes A, B above, a rotation taking B to A also takes A to D and the radial components are comparable as shown. All other linked tangent planes must obey this condition for the same rotation. Thus a trihedron of three planes intersecting the plane of the diagram orthogonally in an equilateral triangle will permit affine rotations of $120°$, but four planes giving a square will again require a $180°$ rotation if opposite sides are to meet the affine comparability condition, which will also be true for more than four planes. We deduce that for a circumscribed regular tetrahedron rotations of $120°$ about axes through the centre and a tangent point will be affine, giving four such axes and a group of eight rotations. Two circumscribed tetrahedra sharing a diametral plane also permit $120°$ rotations about the axis orthogonal to that plane and through opposite vertices, giving only two possible rotations. Of course both these polyhedra also permit $180°$ rotations about any axis.

If instead we concern ourselves with general vector fields in the surface we may seek those transformations which leave their radial components invariant. For a vector AB with A tangential to the surface this requires the plane B to turn about the line such as (BC) in the above diagram, (BC) being invariant. Thus the rate of change of the vector is itself a vector acting tangentially, i.e. is a local rotation, or an overall affine rotation. In the general case we have seen this is restricted to $180°$, obviously with two possible senses.

Another approach is to use surface spherical harmonics (Ref. 28, summarized below) to give us a vector field with the required properties. If the turns τ form a vector field in the surface then it is single-valued if the curl $\nabla x \tau = 0$, in which case τ is the gradient of a scalar field, say $\nabla \psi$. If it is continuous in the surface then the divergence is zero, i.e. $\nabla . \tau = 0$, or $\nabla^2 \psi = 0$ which is Laplace's equation. Solutions of this in the surface are given by the surface spherical harmonics, although in the literature this is treated pointwise. By confining ourselves to changes in the surface we have ensured that the radial component of the changes is zero, which we will prove.

The use of surface spherical harmonics has important advantages if the action is linked to space, as then for a consistent physical situation three conditions must be met:

1. physical quantities must be continuous
2. they must be single-valued
3. they must also be finite

the first two of which we have just seen are met by $\nabla^2 \psi = 0$, as in fact is the third. As an analogy, if a standing wave is to be single-valued round a circle then only certain wavelengths will afford a solution, namely, those for which the circumference is an integral multiple of the wavelength. Surface spherical harmonics provide equivalent solutions for a field over the complete surface of a sphere, which is clearly a more demanding situation. We will first summarize their properties in space where they are expressed in terms of spherical polar co-ordinates (r, θ, ϕ) (see Fig. 58).

The 'longitude' aspect expressed by ϕ is simply a term $\cos(m\phi)$ or $\sin(m\phi)$ for integral m, which may be combined as $e^{im\phi}$. This is closely analogous to the whole-wavelength condition for the simple case of a standing wave on a circle. The conditions for θ are more complicated and relate to Legendre polynomials. Just as Fourier transforms can express a

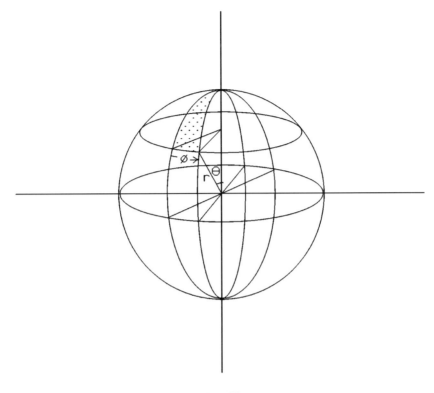

Fig. 58

complicated wave form as a sum of sine waves with suitable phases and amplitudes, so many forms may be expressed as a sum of polynomials provided they form what is called an orthogonal set. Legendre polynomials are such a set, and the first few are

$$P_0(\mu) = 1$$

$$P_1(\mu) = \mu$$

$$P_2(\mu) = \frac{3\mu^2 - 1}{2}$$

$$P_3(\mu) = \frac{5\mu^3 - 3\mu}{2}$$

$$(n + 1)P_{n+1}(\mu) = (2n + 1)\mu P_n(\mu) - nP_{n-1}(\mu)$$

The last line shows the recurrence relation from which higher ones may be deduced, and we note that the highest power of μ in each case is μ^n.

The associated Legendre polynomials are defined as

$$P_n^m(\mu) = (\mu^2 - 1)^{m/2} \frac{d^m P_n(\mu)}{d\mu^m}$$

and when $\mu = \cos\theta$ then Ferrer's form is

$$T_n^m(\mu) = (1 - \mu^2)^{m/2} \frac{d^m P_n(\mu)}{d\mu^m}$$

which is used so that imaginary values are avoided.

Thus $T_2^1 = 3\cos\theta\sqrt{1 - \cos^2\theta} = \dfrac{3\sin(2\theta)}{2}$ and

$T_2^2 = 3(1 - \cos^2\theta) = 3\sin^2\theta$

Figure 59 shows graphs of the first few, and the forms for T_2^1 and T_2^2 above are easily recognized, as are T_0^0, T_1^0 and T_1^1. $T_2^0(\cos\theta) = P_2(\cos\theta) = (3\cos^2\theta - 1)/2 = 3\cos(2\theta)/4 + 1/4$ is recognizable as a distorted $\cos(2\theta)$ plot, as the $+1/4$ term causes the zero to occur at a different angle. The other forms are calculated and plotted similarly.

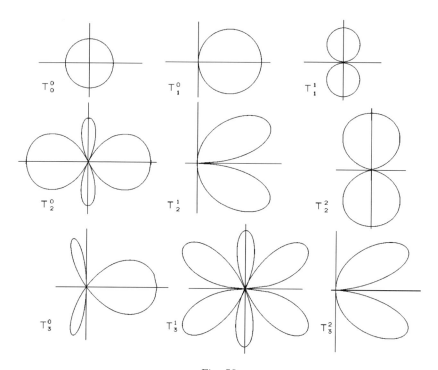

Fig. 59

For example an ellipse with the origin at its centre can be expressed as a weighted sum of these forms, and for an eccentricity of 0.6 the first five even polynomials (i.e. T_{2n}^0, $0 \le n \le 5$) suffice with a deviation of 3×10^{-5}.

These diagrams show a radial plot of the magnitude of the function with angle, and if we rotate them round the vertical axis and simultaneously change their size according to $\cos(m\phi)$ we obtain a picture of the way the magnitudes given by the surface spherical harmonics vary on the sphere. Here m is the superscript of T_n^m and the full expression for the surface spherical harmonics is

$$X_{n,m}(\theta, \phi) = \sqrt{\frac{(2n+1)(n-m)!}{4\pi(n+m)!}}\, T_n^m(\cos\theta)\cos(m\phi)$$

with a similar expression for $Y_{n,m}(\theta, \phi)$, replacing $\cos(m\phi)$ by $\sin(m\phi)$. A suitable function is then expressible as a weighted sum of these harmonics. The first few are:

$$X_{1,0}(\theta, \phi) = \sqrt{\frac{3}{4\pi}}\cos\theta$$

$$X_{1,1}(\theta, \phi) = -\sqrt{\frac{3}{4\pi}}\sin\theta\cos\phi$$

$$X_{2,1}(\theta, \phi) = -\sqrt{\frac{15}{4\pi}}\sin\theta\cos\theta\cos\phi$$

$$X_{2,2}(\theta, \phi) = \sqrt{\frac{15}{16\pi}}\sin^2\theta\cos 2\phi$$

$$X_{3,1}(\theta, \phi) = -\sqrt{\frac{21}{32\pi}}\sin\theta\,(5\cos^2\theta - 1)\cos\phi$$

$$X_{3,2}(\theta, \phi) = \sqrt{\frac{105}{16\pi}}\sin^2\theta\cos\theta\cos 2\phi$$

$$X_{3,3}(\theta, \phi) = -\sqrt{\frac{35}{32\pi}}\sin^3\theta\cos 3\phi$$

noting that $X_{n,0}$ is the same as the Legendre polynomial apart from a constant factor.

For counterspace θ and ϕ are shifts, and the magnitudes are turns. Each such harmonic is itself a solution of Laplace's equation and gives a function that varies in the surface. They are scalar functions of the co-ordinates, so to relate them to vectors we can regard that scalar function as a scalar field ψ, and define a vector field τ such that $\tau = \nabla\psi$, which we know is possible since $\nabla^2\psi = 0$. The standard expression for $\nabla\psi$ in spherical polar coordinates is

$$\nabla\psi = \left\{ \frac{\partial\psi}{\partial r}, \frac{1}{r}\frac{\partial\psi}{\partial\theta}, \frac{1}{r\sin\theta}\frac{\partial\psi}{\partial\phi} \right\}$$

If we set $\psi = X_{n,m}$ then the components of τ are

$$\nabla\psi = \left\{ 0, \frac{k}{\rho}\left[m\cot\theta\, T_n^m(\cos\theta) - T_n^{m+1}(\cos\theta)\right]\cos(m\phi), \right.$$
$$\left. \left\{ \frac{-mk}{\rho\sin\theta}\, T_n^m(\cos\theta)\sin(m\phi)\right\} \right\} \tag{1}$$

where $k = \sqrt{\dfrac{(2n+1)(n-m)!}{4\pi(n+m)!}}$ and ρ is the polar radius of the sphere.

The radial component is thus zero, which is what we require giving us a tangential vector field. Thus we can find time–invariant vector fields to suit the requirements of a large range of scalar fields by expressing each such field as a series of spherical harmonics.

In the theory of Legendre functions (Ref. 28) the series for $P_n^m(\mu)$ only converges if n is an integer, which is thus also true both for $T_n^m(\mu)$ and the spherical harmonics. It is clear that m must also be an integer for there to be single-valued solutions in the surface, and also $m \le n$.

Thus for $X_{1,0}$, for example, the above expression for $\nabla\psi$ gives the vector field

$$\left\{ 0, -\sqrt{\frac{3}{4\pi}}\,\frac{\sin\theta}{\rho}, 0 \right\} \tag{2}$$

which is like the diagram above for T_1^1 rotated about the vertical axis, so that the turn vectors have zero magnitude on the 'equator' and a maximum at the poles for all values of ϕ. Recall that this is a vector field, not a set of position vectors, so that the zero radius term does not mean that the magnitude is zero but that the radial component is zero as explained before. The magnitude increases with decreasing ρ, so the smaller the sphere (i.e. the larger Euclideanly speaking) the greater the magnitude.

The involvement of harmonics and of the numbers n, m suggests that the ether described by this kind of time-invariance is the chemical ether, which Rudolf Steiner also described as the tone ether and the number ether. Note in this respect the rhythmic variation of the magnitude of the turns in the above field for $X_{1,0}$, which is evidently present in ever greater complexity for higher order harmonics. We see how this approach gives the analogue of standing waves in the surface, the amplitude of the wave being the magnitude of the turn as shown by the graphs of T_n^m, and that they are longitudinal waves in the surface since the radial component is zero. This further reinforces the interpretation of the ether as the tone ether. We have yet to interpret the meaning of non-radial turns, which are the 'substance' of this ether. Our proposal that the ethers be related to such time-invariant transformations in counterspace thus captures what Steiner found through his research and indicates why this ether has these various characteristics.

A prolate spheroid can appear as a sphere to two CSIs at its foci (see Appendix 6), so that if ϕ is the angle about the major axis then it is possible for a field of turns given by the surface spherical harmonics to appear the same to both CSIs, provided the turn at θ equals that at $180 - \theta$. We illustrate this for $X_{1,0}$ in Fig. 60.

The two CSIs are at O_1 and O_2, the spheroid is represented by the ellipse, and the graph of T_1^1 (c.f. (2) above) is shown by pairs of small circles as it is seen by each CSI. The radial distances O_1P_1 and O_2P_2 represent the

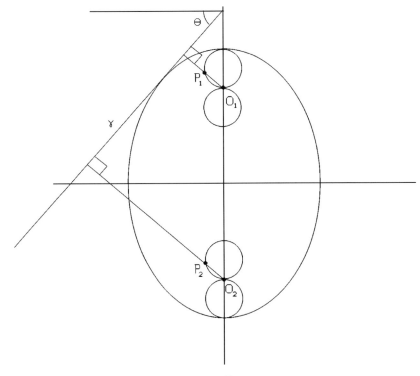

Fig. 60

magnitudes of the tangential turns in the tangent plane γ, which are thus equal.

A similar argument holds good for all the harmonics as they are all symmetrical wrt θ and $(180 - \theta)$, so it will also apply to combinations of them if some special underlying scalar field is analysed into a series of harmonics. For the above case there is complete rotational symmetry about the major axis, but $\cos(m\phi)$ will impose restrictions on that orientation for $m > 0$ so that the rotational symmetry will be quantized, the number of possible zero-strain orientations depending upon m. One problem in (1) is that the third component of the vector has $\sin \theta$ in the denominator which is zero for $\theta = 0$ and $180°$. However, $T_n^m (\cos \theta)/\sin \theta$ may be regarded as having a finite limit because $T_n^m (\cos \theta)$ always has a $\sin \theta$ term in the numerator for $m > 0$.

This gives us an indication of how chemical action may relate to this ether when linked to space, since pairs of CSIs as above only occur in linkages. We need to postulate some structure for a counterspace to take the idea further, which will be imaged in its CSIs, so that two CSIs from different populations may or may not be able to relate according to their structure. If this structure is expressed by a harmonic configuration then the possibility of a relationship between CSIs as above depends upon that structure.

Thus we propose that

A primal counterspace has a structure expressed by a combination of surface spherical harmonics.

This is a working proposal which needs further elaboration, and is not meant to exclude further contributions to the structure from other ethers. It brings us into relation with conventional atomic theory where the atomic orbitals relate directly to surface spherical harmonics, so that the s-orbitals are for $n = 0$ with one possible value of m (n is as defined above, not the principal quantum number; in atomic theory the symbol 1 is usually used for our n), the p-orbitals are for $n = 1$ for which there are three values of m *viz.* $-1, 0, 1$ giving six distinct states if each is associated with two possible spin states, the d-orbitals are for $n = 2$ with five possible values of m, and so on. Orbitals also incorporate a radial aspect given by the Laguerre polynomials which we have not considered as we are explicitly concerned here with non–radial aspects, but which may be expected to arise if we relate light and chemistry. We are not espousing a particle-theory here and it should be clear that our route has led us to consider the use of surface spherical harmonics for reasons other than those of quantum theory.

Our discussion above suggests that the element of linkage between space and counterspace for this ether is a spheroid with a surface wave structure, so that the ether concerns *bonding* (rather than chemical analysis, see Ref. 31). If two CSIs are related as above we need to consider the size of the spheroid involved. We saw in (1) that the magnitude of the vector field is inversely proportional to the polar radius ρ of the counterspace sphere, and will thus be minimized for very large values of ρ, i.e. for very small spheroids spatially speaking. If there were a necessity for the magnitude to be as small as possible then this would show why this ether is contractive in character as indicated by Steiner (Ref. 34). But, our above proposal entails the idea that a CSI has a structure of its own, at least partially expressed by harmonics, before it becomes involved in a bond. The basis for this structure is not, on our present view, chemical as it concerns a single CSI whereas our bonding proposal concerns at least two. That suggests either a combination of harmonics in one surface or the involvement of several concentric spheres. When the basis for this is clearer we will be able to take the chemistry further.

In accordance with our overall concept we see the chemical ether in the context of polar special affine geometry, so that the confinement to the surface of a sphere in a non-expansive manner accords with that. We also recall, however, that a sphere cannot be distinguished from general ellipsoids in affine geometry, so that the method of harmonic analysis will need to be extended to such surfaces. Thus a sphere will be equivalent in polar special affine geometry to any ellipsoid with the same polar volume, which will include what look like Euclidean hyperboloids. The turns making up the field in the surface are not comparable in different directions unless each direction is referred to some overall affinely acceptable reference. However this eases the extension to harmonics in the surface of an ellipsoid as there is no difference from a sphere, so that the spherical analysis thus suffices.

We have seen that a counterspace sphere may appear in space as a prolate spheroid, which was derived in an essentially metric manner. For a general ellipsoid there is a focal conic, and if the CSI lies on this conic then every elliptic cross-section containing it can be regarded as circular in counterspace, as for the major cross-sections of a prolate spheroid, and since their relative polar radii are non-comparable at the affine level the ellipsoid can still be seen as equivalent to a sphere.

To interpret the turn vectors as a field in the surface we seem to have little option but to adopt a reference sphere and relate their magnitudes to that. The polar volume, which *is* invariant, must at the special affine level serve as our basic reference, giving ρ for that sphere, and hence an interpretation of the magnitudes. Thus the linkage tensor for this ether may be a trivector, which has volume or polar volume as its basic invariant magnitude.

When linked to metric space we see that this ether may give rise to quite complex configurations since the ratio of the surface area of an ellipsoid to its volume is not a trivial calculation unless it is prolate or oblate, and the harmonics may relate to a non-spherical surface. Whether the solution of elliptic functions can be facilitated by reference to counterspace seems an interesting purely mathematical question.

In chemistry four bonds are known, namely, the hydrogen, covalent, metallic and electrovalent bonds. We have seen one kind of bond based on harmonics and in Chapter 14 another kind based on a trapped photon. The latter will become evident in the next chapter on the life ether.

In Fig. 60 the two CSIs see the spheroid rotated by 180° wrt each other, which implies an intrinsic rotation or spin between the two CSIs in the sense that their linkage between space and counterspace differs by 180°. This raises the whole question of the orientation of a linkage. In general for affine geometry we have seen that only 180° rotations are possible if vectors are to be invariant, so that is the only possible linkage orientation apart from a direct one. This implies an interesting interpretation of spin, namely, as the orientation between space and counterspace for a linkage. The term spin implies a permanently acting orientation which is however not a rotation as such. Thus for two CSIs to relate as in Fig. 60 they must have opposite spin in this sense.

At the beginning of this chapter we also found other ways in which finite numbers of tangent planes may form an affine rotation group, *viz.* a trihedron, a tetrahedron and a pair of tetrahedra, all permitting rotations of 120°. This suggests another possible spin orientation which could be expressed as a spin of 1/3 if the above case is 1/2.

Although no actual chemistry has been treated in this chapter, the basis for that has been laid by discovering the nature of the chemical ether with its rhythmic and numerical properties, and pointing the way to approach bonding.

16. LIFE

We have explored two kinds of time invariance, for light and chemistry, and based on our proposal that the ethers are two-dimensional we now need to see what kind of invariance applies to life where the linkage is fully metric. In the previous chapter we came to the point of postulating a harmonic structure for a counterspace which will manifest in connection with a single CSI, but whether this relates only to a single surface or to nested surfaces is an open question. Also, we need to find out what the surface relates to and what determines its size.

Before we start it is perhaps worth mentioning that we do not expect to derive any of the living forms of nature from this ether, but rather the processes it provides to support their appearance. Equally we make no assumptions about that, i.e. we proceed to find out what this ether does regardless of other ideas about the genesis of living forms.

So far we have confined ourselves to direct linkages such as points and planes being simultaneously in both spaces, and we noted early on that the only transformation that is strain-free for such linkages is rotation about an axis through the CSI. Another kind of strain-free transformation is a polarity, for if a counterspace structure of planes is linked by a polarity to a spatial structure of points then a metric transformation of the counterspace structure induces a metric transformation of the spatial one. The same will apply to rates of change. This may be significant for the life ether where we are concerned with metric linkages.

What is inside a surface has a different meaning in counterspace, for inside refers to the planes that for a Euclidean perspective are outside. When we considered gases, liquids and gravity we analysed the affine and shift strain for what amounts to a common 'inside' from the counterspace perspective. We have not looked at strain for what is 'outside' a surface for counterspace. For economy of expression we will write '*inside*' when we mean it in the counterspace sense, and 'inside' when we mean that spatially. The primal counterspaces implied by our work so far have had a cosmic character in this sense. Living organisms exhibit many formative features that suggest they each have their own counterspace that is distinct from these all-pervading cosmic ones, as shown in Ref. 4. The question then is how these relate to the cosmic ones, for they bring substance into a different kind of order from that observed in the mineral realm, with self-organizing properties, growth and decay, nourishment and so on. Surfaces thus seem to be important and we know that membranes play a vital and ubiquitous role in living organisms in this respect, their semi- and selective-permeable properties being of utmost importance, e.g. in protecting the brain from poisons, allowing the cell to function properly and so on. The rates of diffusion of substances across their surfaces are of fundamental importance. The number of cellular structures containing membranes increases with increasing complexity of an organism. The membrane seems to be a phenomenological expression of the significance of surfaces which we will now be guided by. In space the membrane establishes an environment inside itself, which is *outside* for counterspace. Thus we see an inversion is required if the counterspace inside is to be related to the spatial inside. This suggests that a polarity is operative so that the planar structure of the ether may relate to the pointwise activity inside the membrane, and the action of that polarity at the surface is critical. *Prima facie* there is no mathematical superiority in the incidence of a point and plane, such as occurs for a polarity at the self-polar surface (or SPS for short), compared with any other polar pair, but taking membranes as our guide it seems to deserve some attention. In passing we note that membranes are never truly spherical, the plasma membrane perhaps approaching that more than any other, and most are far from it. However the affine quality of surfaces described in the previous chapter allows them to be related to the ideal mathematical concept more readily. The affine aspect should also relate to the semi-permeability of a surface where the metric and the affine need not coincide rigidly.

Incidence is preserved by projective transformations, so they will also preserve the incidence of points and planes at a surface. We would then see the surface as the effective arena for the relationship between the planar aspects of the ether and those aspects of substance that relate to points, or better said, location in space. This also helps us with another potential difficulty, for metric relationships are the most rigid, also for counterspace. A metric structure in counterspace would seem to be the antithesis of the qualities of life, but if this metric quality is confined to surface action then this is overcome. Thus the two-dimensionality of this ether seems to be expressed in this way. However, it should not be imagined that in real organisms we have true mathematical surfaces; they have of course some thickness, albeit of the order of only 7×10^{-9} m.

Returning to the rate of diffusion across a membrane we gain a clue to the way time comes into the picture we are now developing, for this is indeed a radial activity. The radial component of a vector in the surface represents a time interval which may relate to the diffusion rate. This introduces an additional factor to the chemical one which is tangential.

If a polarity is active as postulated, a turn vector will be transformed into a shift gradient for which the time component will be radial and the chemical component tangential. We have always treated location in space, which the polarity relates to a plane, as being that of a CSI, so that the shift gradient will be like those we have studied before. In particular in Chapter 11 we saw this in relation to impulse, so that the polarity will transform the time component into a change of impulse, i.e. a force. In this way the life ether acts on substance in a surface. This connects the counterspace of the organism to the fractally related CSIs of the substance it ingests.

There are many types of membrane in a higher organism with different transport systems and different kinds of permeability, affecting different substances. Potassium and sodium are basic, e.g. to the plasma membrane, but calcium and amino acids are involved in others and many enzymes are involved throughout. Water is also transported across membranes either in bulk or by diffusion or both. The structure of membranes involves lipids and proteins with properties also governing the transport systems. The relation of time intervals to a diffusion force is thus not sufficiently specific, and one type of counterspace for an organism does not by itself account for the varieties of membrane. As we would expect there is a high degree of organization and differentiation involved, an overall aspect of which is the nesting of membranes within each other so that mitochondria, the nucleus and organelles like the chloroplasts have membranes inside the plasma membrane of the cell—not to mention the many organs such as the kidneys and intestines inside the skin. The way the life ether relates to these details is thus of great interest.

We expect the structures of the counterspaces of the substances involved to be such that they may be integrated into a living organism by the life ether, and we now suggest that the detailed structure of those counterspaces is also governed by the life ether, for the chemical aspect alone as we have developed it so far is insufficient. *In other words life does not change the laws governing substances when they are incorporated in organisms, but rather it is integral to their nature in the first place.* The addition of a vital principle over and above the substances is not necessary as the life ether is involved from the start. Thus far we accept the argument against the vitalists, but we recognize that holistic aspects of the world have a real basis, in the ethers, rather than being mere epiphenomena. This is clearly not to espouse materialism, but to recognize the part of their viewpoint which is valid. The work of researchers such as Goodwin (Ref. 16) can also be seen in the light of our approach.

We are led to look at the structure of substance in the light of what we have seen so far of the activity of the life ether, continuing from where we left it in the last chapter. The essential new aspects are the way life ether relates to surfaces, its nested approach to organization, and its conversion of time intervals into force. Already we found for the chemical aspect that surfaces are significant, but we found no basis for their actual existence. We now postulate that the life ether imparts to the structure of a counterspace a definite surface with metric properties (as the life ether concerns the metric of counterspace) which ideally is a sphere, and that it may add to the tangential harmonic field in that surface a radial component. In addition the harmonic structure may include nested surfaces with similar properties. We find we are very close indeed to the kind of picture attributed to hypothetical atoms. But we must stress that we envisage a cosmic structure in the ether which is imaged in CSIs; we do not envisage assemblages of material particles as is normally conceived. However, we must acknowledge that in this century physics has made big strides away from simplistic material pictures to thought structures so subtle that they cannot be pictured at all, the various models employed being but crutches to help manipulate the mathematics. The Copenhagen Interpretation of quantum physics, resisted by Einstein and Bohm among others, underlies that and forms an important bridging situation from materialism through mathematism to a possible new way of thinking. For all its shortcomings so eloquently but fruitlessly fought against by Einstein, it does have that merit.

Our closeness to the conventional view is to be expected as we do not expect all the experimental work of this century to prove to be rubbish, nor would we wish to imply that. The Standard Model of physics is based on enormous effort and investment, and in line with our earlier results we may hope to find what underlies it even if we do not espouse it, for its structural aspects must have something in common with reality or it would not work at all. A possible interpretation of the wave function in terms of our chemical ether harmonics, to be considered in a later chapter, points in that direction.

What does a particular population of CSIs underlie? We can immediately imagine either that it relates to a chemical element or to a more basic entity such as a proton or electron. It may be recalled that in Chapter 11 we pointed out that different substances must have different scalings between space and counterspace, and this underlay our approach to Snell's Law for refraction. This requires that each element in any case belongs to a different primal counterspace, which together with the analysis of harmonic structure in the last chapter and its obvious relation to the conventional concept of orbitals suggests most strongly that we identify populations of CSIs with the different chemical elements. The nested concept of the conventional atom fits our life ether approach to nested structure, for example, but the latter reflects a cosmic structure rather than a particulate one. We will proceed on this basis.

We thus envisage a definite boundary to a CSI within which there is harmonic structure, ideally a sphere but polarization may change that. Its size will correspond to the size of a conventional atom, and it will be recalled that this is of the same order of magnitude for all atoms and shows some degree of rhythm wrt atomic number. This however only applies to CSIs, not to the primal counterspace of the element. The structure of the surface and whether it images the permeability properties of membranes in some way is an interesting question. In Chapters 5 and 8 we introduced CSIs as fractal images of their primal counterspace, and we related the fractalization to a 'tearing of space' in relation to the sun. Taking the surface of the sun as an archetype we expect some image of its surface in those we are now proposing for CSIs, in other words the permeability has to do with the exchange of radiation with its surroundings. This will also apply to any nested surfaces.

There will be a vector field of turns and any radial component will relate to 'diffusion', i.e. radiation. Thus in the steady state there should be no nett radial component of the field. In this sense the life ether imposes a time invariance in the surface in the form of a zero surface integral wrt the normal, which by Gauss's Theorem

$$\int_s \tau.\mathbf{ds} = \int_v \nabla.\tau\mathbf{dv}$$

will imply a zero divergence *inside* the surface (see Appendix 3). Our approach to light suggests that although for membranes the vector field is polar-transformed to a force, for a CSI it will ultimately relate to the polar area of a cone. The question then is how to relate the two to account for emission and absorption. From the above comment on Gauss's Theorem a photon cone may represent a non-zero divergence *inside* the surface after emission until it has assumed cylindrical form, so that it will relate to the surface integral. We assume tacitly that once the photon has assumed cylindrical form it has become dissociated from the CSI and the latter will revert to equilibrium in its surface. If it is intercepted before that happens then a relationship will be established between the intercepting CSI and the source, which may then be transformed by the polarity of the life ether into a shift gradient between the two CSIs, i.e. into a force. Thus we find one possible basis for photons to mediate forces as in conventional physics. The life ether thus works at this level in the relationship between the tangential and radial aspects of the surface field.

If two CSIs suffer strain due to non-aligned harmonic fields, a non-zero surface integral may arise in the above sense causing divergence and the sharing of a photon cone. This represents a quite different kind of bond from the one based on harmonics that was treated in the previous chapter and in fact was foreshadowed in Chapter 14. It will be 'virtual' in the sense that the photon is not radiant but trapped, and will be associated with a definite frequency as we saw in Chapter 14. Gauss's Theorem enables a quantitative relationship to be found between the polar area of the photon cone regarded as a divergence and the surface integral of the radial component of the turn field.

We are now concerned with the metric aspects of the surfaces which purely chemically were treated affinely. In a metric linkage a prolate spheroid, for example, will acquire a radial component to its field as seen in space even though for counterspace it remains a sphere. The second focus is then interesting as it is a location at which the spheroid can also appear as a sphere in counterspace, possibly giving rise to virtual CSI effects. It is also possible for the surface to become properly ellipsoidal with the CSI at the centre, now that we are concerned with metric aspects, which would represent permanent polarization. In this case some interesting relationships arise as a prolate spheroid in space is oblate in counterspace and vice versa. For an oblate spheroid in counterspace we have a focal cylinder which is thus like another species of trapped photon. We expect a divergence *inside* its polar volume as the polarization implies a radial imbalance of the turn field in the surface, and this cylinder is the best candidate for that as it is inherently related to the polarization and focal planes are the planes of divergence (see Appendix 3). Thus we approach a basis for the electrical properties of matter. What is normally referred to as an electron is probably this focal cylinder, which fits in well with Steiner's description of electricity as 'fallen light' (Ref. 33). Ionization would detach this cylinder, requiring the surface integral to remain unchanged as the divergence remains, but the focal cylinder to be lost. This could be achieved by shifting the CSI to a focus so that the spheroid reverts to a sphere in counterspace. Thus a positive charge would be associated with such a spheroid while the detached cylinder would carry a negative one. Ionization by the capture of an electron cylinder would *impose* a polarization on a surface. It would seem that an electron cylinder differs from a photon cylinder in having mass in line with the experiments of Sir J.J. Thomson. However Thomson's experiment did not really prove the existence of *rest mass* but rather that of momentum, so we hold this question open. If we come to agree with the conventional idea that an electron has rest mass then its cylinder will have the property that when detached it can exist as a cone which does not have to expand to a cylinder in the way a photon cone does. The possibility of multiple ionization suggests that there are at least as many nested surfaces in a CSI as there are degrees of ionization since a spheroid can only have one focal cylinder, which is an important clue to the further elucidation of the structure of a counterspace. However caution is also necessary at this stage as ionization could occur in stages so that a surface could become ionized a first time, and then undergo further change for a second ionization.

Electrical polarization and ionization play an important part in the action of membranes, so this development of the properties of CSIs relates to that action rather well, as indeed it should if—as we have suggested—the life ether establishes the metric structure of elements in accordance with the requirements of organisms.

The other possible type of polarized spheroid is prolate in counterspace and oblate in space. This does not have a focal cylinder in counterspace but two focal planes instead. If it occurs it represents some other process quite different from electrical polarization. It will have a focal ring in space instead of two foci.

In the last chapter we considered spin in relation to the orientation of a linkage for the affine case. Now we need to develop this for the metric case. A transformation leaves the absolutes invariant as a whole, but a homography between the points of one and the tangent planes of the other is quite possible. This is essentially expressed by the scaling tensor $\mathbf{J}$ which must be involved when the polarity of the life ether transforms a turn vector into a shift gradient and hence a force. Indeed $\mathbf{J}$ seems itself to express the polarity. The spin representations of the orthogonal group give rise to tensors called *spinors* which were discovered by Cartan (Ref. 7), and we need tensors for the usual reasons. They are briefly reviewed in Appendix 7, and one important fact is that they are metric entities and have no analogue in affine geometry. A possible interpretation of them is given in Appendix 7 which relates the absolutes of space and counterspace and is thus relevant now. This implies one particular homography relating the points of the absolute circle to the tangent planes of the absolute cone, one spinor for each corresponding pair. This effects the linkage as the same spinor can apply to both absolutes. We expect this to express angular momentum.

When the SPS is not spherical in both spaces then strain-free polarities are given by the possible mutual polarities, i.e. those polar pairs which are polar for both types of quadric. Thus if we have a prolate spheroid in space and a sphere in counterspace then only certain polar pairs are simultaneously polar for both. Given two quadrics α and β these mutual polarities are given by the eigenvectors of the matrix $\beta^{-1}\alpha$, if α and β are also the matrices representing the quadrics. For a polarized prolate spheroid with the CSI at the centre the mutual polar pairs are as follows:

Ω and the centre,
the plane in the centre containing the circular cross-section and the point in Ω polar to it,
the principal axis of symmetry s of the spheroid as a line of poles together with the pencil of parallel planes orthogonal to s,

and

the planes in *s* together with the points in Ω polar to them (which lie on the line in Ω polar to *s*).

Furthermore, two distinct spheroids in space sharing their principal axis of symmetry *s* share the polarities of planes in *s* with their poles in Ω. If they do not intersect they also have two planes orthogonal to *s* together with their poles, the easiest example of which is when they touch so that their mutual tangent plane and point of contact form a mutually polar pair. Otherwise they look like this (Fig. 61):

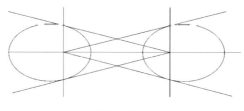

Fig. 61

These are mutually polar both for the two CSIs and for each CSI internally. In this way, just in connection with the life ether, we begin to approach a basis for crystal structure based on bonds which are not chemical. This particularly arises for polarized CSIs, i.e. in connection with electricity which plays such an important role in crystal structure. For the life ether we have seen that polarities of incident point-and-plane pairs are significant, so that the case where the two spheroids are in contact is particularly interesting, and an array of CSIs is then easily visualized sharing lattice planes each of which belongs to many mutual polarities. This sharing suggests an economy of polarities which may relate to the rigidity of the structure. The typical spacing of close packed crystals agrees with this approach as we expect the major axis to exceed the Bohr radius. There are 13 types of pencil of quadrics (Ref. 39) many of which are relevant to this subject and require more exploration, as mutual polarities may be regarded as members of such pencils.

Returning to the possibility of a homography between the absolutes we saw that spinors require one particular homography, but for a more general homography we can have a spin which for a metric coupling need not be restricted to 180° as was necessary in the affine case, as lengths are comparable in all directions in metric geometry. This leads to a correlation that includes rotation and is more general than the polarity. Now the polarity from counterspace to space, transforming a plane into a point, relates to the counterspace version of the SPS while the reverse transformation from space to counterspace relates to the spatial version of it. If the SPS is not a sphere in both spaces then these two transformations will be different. A rhythmic process between the two spaces involving first one and then the other transformation will lead to path curves, especially if that transformation is a correlation involving rotation (see Appendix 8).

If we consider a whole organism in relation to this then we have an interesting situation wrt inside and *inside* which brings us back to fractals. For a membrane, particularly the plasma membranes of the cells of an organism, all other cells of the organism are *inside* it. *Thus we begin to see what makes an organism an organism: it is inside every cell for counterspace so that each cell relates to the whole organism just for that reason.* This kind of relationship is just what fractals are about, for the images of the organism seen by every cell must differ for a many-celled organism and yet they need to be in synergy. Fractals provide a way in which such synergy may be described mathematically, which may explain why organisms often have fractal forms. If an organism is injured the synergy will be partially disrupted and then healing occurs as it reinstates itself. If the organism is not in balance, e.g. at the beginning of its life, it grows towards synergy. This implies a two-way traffic between counterspace and space such as was suggested in the previous paragraph. Furthermore path curves are involved in fractals, for recalling the chaos-game (Chapter 5) we saw that for a particular form there is a set of linear transformations (tiles) which acting together give the form. If the random number generator should get 'stuck' so that the same tile is selected each time then the points would follow a spiral path curve. This shows that the actual fractal is woven of path curves such that those points on the path curves survive which are in synergy for the total process. It is quite conceivable that fundamental forms may only involve one three-dimensional 'tile', which would give the path curve forms described by Edwards (Ref. 11, and see Appendix 8). These apply ubiquitously to the forms of eggs and plant buds, to the left ventricle of the heart, and to the uterus in pregnancy.

In Chapter 14 the concept of a 'gauge strain threshold' (GST) was introduced at which there is a scaling discontinuity and hence a discontinuity wrt time. Outside this threshold we have a stable relation to time which we have relied upon to account for refraction and generally for the non-living aspects of physics. If we identify this with the SPS then in the mineral realm we imagine for these reasons that it is very small spatially speaking. However there is no *a priori* reason for assigning any particular size to it, and that must ultimately depend on the kind of linkage. We have seen that for the life ether we are concerned with polarity where the significance of inside and outside differs. For minerals the time invariance required is that the GST is small, but this need not be the case for counterspaces associated with living organisms. The linkage associated with life would appear to change it so that fractal effects, growth measures and path curves appear macroscopically (e.g. in ferns and phyllotaxis generally), unlike crystals and mineral forms generally which exhibit step measures. We suggest that the aspect of time invariance controlled by the life ether relates to the GST, which may be larger than for minerals, e.g. the size of a cell membrane. A relation between the warmth and life ethers arises as the former controls scaling while the latter controls the GST. Homeostasis may be a phenomenon arising from this for more complex linkages where the synergy depends upon a definite scaling inside the GST and hence a definite temperature. It is interesting that this view of things sees 'mineral' as a condition of life: a particular kind of time invariance (the GST) imposed by the life ether governing the lifeless. This may entail a change in the way we regard the 'lifeless', for it is after all related to the life ether and we begin perhaps to make contact with the 'Gaia hypothesis' in a new way. Instead of invoking merely physically based feedback loops in ecosystems the synergy-based ones of the life ether are also involved. This view of the mineral is consistent with our earlier claim that the structure of chemical elements is governed by the life ether.

That the mineral involves no homeostasis on the one hand, while the higher animal does on the other, suggests that the relation between the warmth and life ethers governs the distinction between the various kingdoms of life. The plants involve a change in the GST but not the warmth conditions. The transition from plant to animal need not involve the warmth ether, however, as evidenced by the reptiles and other cold-blooded animals. Among multicellular organisms plants, fungi and animals are distinguished by their mode of nutrition, the plants employing photosynthesis, the fungi absorption and the animals ingestion. These differences are reflected in the cell structure. We see here a polarity between inside and *inside*, with fungi in an intermediate position. This polarity arises without homeostasis in view of the existence of cold-blooded animals.

This chapter has described the state of the research-in-progress on the life aspects of the whole enterprise related in this book. There are many 'mays' and 'coulds' because the work is not far enough advanced to be more definite. The aim to integrate the different lines of investigation described in the various chapters into one whole looks promising here, which is one reason why it seemed justified to present such an unfinished picture.

17. QUANTUM PHYSICS

Quantum physics developed in response to experimental results that could not be accounted for by classical physics. The first and most famous was the spectral distribution of the radiation from an incandescent object that did not fit classical predictions, which Max Planck accounted for by assuming the radiation is emitted in quanta. Classical physics assumed that matter is composed of small massive particles and attempted to explain phenomena by reduction to the behaviour of minute particles which behave like ordinary balls, having mass, momentum, position and so on. Essentially this failed, and when the difficulties posed by experimental findings were most intense Einstein said: 'It was as if the ground had been pulled out from under one, with no firm foundation to be seen anywhere upon which to build' (Ref. 26). Pauli said: 'At the moment physics is again terribly confused. In any case, it is too difficult for me, and I wish I had been a movie comedian or something of the sort and never had heard of physics' (Ref. 20). Quantum physics textbooks still begin by assuming that there are protons, electrons and so forth having the basic properties of small balls and then derive their more bizarre behaviour on that foundation (e.g. Refs. 5, 13 and 24), so that in analysing the hydrogen atom for example the electron is regarded as a particle on a sphere, its Hamiltonian is constructed and then the resulting equations are solved using surface spherical harmonics, Laguerre polynomials and so forth. The concepts spin and orbital angular momentum are derived by analogy from a planetry model of the atom, even though the results bear little resemblance to that model. The orbitals conceived on the basis of quantum mechanics are so unlike an orbit that if one 'steps back' and looks hard one must surely say that the notion of an orbit is altogether inappropriate, in which case it is illogical to base anything on the classical concepts either of angular momentum due to orbital motion or of spin. This is borne out by the concept of spin based on spinors which has no classical counterpart and defies visualization. It would seem preferable to find out what the true foundations of physics are rather than appeal to materialistic analogies which creak at the seams. This is easy to say and hard to accomplish, and these comments are not intended to criticize the brilliant work of all from Schrödinger onwards but rather to accept what it is that the results seem to be saying to us: radically new concepts and a new way of thinking are needed (Refs. 25 and 43). The formal aspects may well prove to be similar, but the thinking lying behind them needs to be different.

We will now outline some indications given by the present work for a fresh look at quantum physics for which we have found several pointers.

Wave-Particle Duality

Our approach to photon cones removes this duality and opens up a way of approaching the paradoxical aspect of EPR-style experiments. So far light has been approached based on an unstructured photon cylinder, although hints at a further development of this were indicated in Chapter 14.

Uncertainty Relationship

Heisenberg's Uncertainty Principle is fundamental to quantum physics, and we have seen pointers to it several times. The most basic notion is that when a measurement is made a transition is often thereby induced from an affine to a metric linkage, i.e. measurement renders it *metric*. This may involve a conflict if dimensions that are affinely consistent cannot be metrically consistent, requiring only one to become measurable which the experimental conditions dictate. For example the bivector representing a photon cylinder may have to change type, resulting in an unmeasurable polar area. Thus as in quantum physics the act of measuring changes the situation irreversibly.

A far-reaching aspect arose in Chapter 14 where Penrose's R-operator was related to the realignment of the scalings inside and outside a GST, which when analysed may be expected to show that the 'collapse' involved has the above effect. Furthermore, the 'retreat inwards' of a CSI after a measurement may have the effect of rendering the location of the CSI imprecise as the scaling inside the GST progressively diverges from that outside it.

Wave Function

The requirement for surface spherical harmonics in Chapter 15 has very interesting analogues with quantum mechanics. The mathematics and the requirements for quantization are the same as those arising from the conventional analysis of a hydrogen atom, and further development of the ideas in this book may reveal an ever closer formal relationship. When Schrödinger proposed his wave function he suggested it be solved by separating the variables to give a time-independent wave equation and a separate time-dependent one. In conventional theory this is simply a well-tried mathematical device rather than a requirement of the basic physics. What the waves *are* is unclear. Certainly there seem to be no actual physical waves represented by them, yet the method is remarkably fruitful—another case of an analogy working out well for reasons that are unclear. Born suggested the interpretation that the square of the amplitude be related to the probability distribution of the location of the particle involved.

Our approach starts with a definite reason for finding a time-independent process as described in Chapter 15, so that this is not based on mathematical convenience but has a rationale. We found wavelike behaviour associated with the chemical ether, which is neither physical nor particulate and thus it is no surprise that the waves have no physical counterpart as such. The wave equation may thus describe an aspect of the rhythms of the chemical ether. These waves are like longitudinal standing waves in a surface, consisting of a vector field described by turns. Thus the boundaries giving rise to them are not physical potential wells but the fact that the surfaces in counterspace are closed. The shape of those surfaces will control the wave components involved.

One extraordinary aspect of quantum mechanics is the need to relate standing waves to discontinuities, e.g. at the edges of a potential well. A successful cut-and-try technique has been to fit an exponential decay to a wave which matches its gradient and amplitude at the 'join'; if such cannot be found then no solution for that wave exists (e.g. Ref. 13). The *ad hoc* nature of this procedure may be replaceable by another when the detailed contribution to the standing waves caused by non-spherical surfaces in counterspace is further investigated. This would replace the Born-style adjustment to the probabilities caused by the exponential components.

Thus we envisage the appeal back to classical analogues such as Bohr's model being replaced by a treatment of the rhythmic quality and discreteness of the chemical ether, coupled with the structure of a counterspace when that has been further elucidated. The link back to classical quantities such as momentum and force will be achieved via the above model for the R-operator rather than by an uneasy parallelism between the scaled-down classical and the quantum descriptions. The relation between momentum and frequency exhibited in Chapter 11 is interesting as conventionally this is an entirely non-classical result.

Collapse of the Wave Function

The R-operator is essentially a reference to the collapse of the wavefunction when a measurement is made or an interaction occurs. We suggested in Chapter 14 that this is related to a realignment of the scalings inside and outside the GST for such events. The collapse usually envisaged is that a measurable is rendered more or less precise so that the probabilities associated with the wave-function amplitude cease to exist at the moment of the interaction. We are not espousing a statistical interpretation such as Born's, and we envisage instead that an equilibrium of the surface waves may be altered by the interaction leading to the measurables manifesting in a particular way. Afterwards the CSI(s) 'retreat inwards' leading to the re-establishment of the waves again. This is a development area to be pursued in future.

Orbitals

The fact that surface spherical harmonics describe the non-radial aspects of conventional orbitals, and the requirement for their use in characterizing the chemical ether, shows a close link of this work to quantum physics. As remarked before, this suggests that the structure of a CSI is built up from such harmonics. Our approach is in a sense 'purer' as it does not start from hypothetical particles which then cannot be thought consistently. Instead we see a wave-structure of an element which can be forced into having radial components of the waves and thus become electrified in the way outlined in Chapter 16.

Spin

We interpreted 'spin' as a fixed orientation of a linkage between the metric absolutes of space and counterspace, mediated by spinors as the appropriate tensors. This seems preferable to trying to imagine a particle-that-is-not-really-a-particle spinning in any classical way; indeed it is well known that spin cannot be thought of in this way, although the notion and name arose originally from such a thought. Thus it seems desirable to find out what it really is rather than leave it in such an undefined conceptual state, and the approach suggested seems helpful.

Bose-Einstein Statistics

In Ref. 24 an interesting point is made about the use of Bose-Einstein statistics in quantum physics: they apply to particles that are literally identical, *including their position in space*. What interests us in the present context is not the statistics but the fact that for bosons it is necessary to think in this way. The idea that they behave (it is thought) as if they are coincident is not easy to interpret in a purely physical way. Our postulate that CSIs are images of a primal counterspace seems to capture this idea and interpret it in a new way that dissolves this difficulty. It is an interesting pointer to further developments of the work.

Non-locality and Fields

The test of Bell's Inequality by Aspect used entangled photons. In Chapter 13 it was found that photons do not travel, and that the interaction between a source and an illuminated object is more mutual than is usually thought in view of our interpretation of time, i.e. the relation between the two mediated by a photon cone is in a sense instantaneous. Attempts to relate it to time then embroil the relationship between reciprocal turn and distance, a factor in counterspace which reflects back into space as a time interval when related to a physical measurement. Thus the non-locality is in counterspace, not in space. The use of entangled photons in the test is an experimental technique to demonstrate this.

Non-locality is an essential feature of our fractal approach to counterspace. Work is in hand to see how this relates to fields, as it seems that effects such as polarization may be mediated fractally via a primal counterspace rather than by 'lines of force'. This is an attractive idea as the mysterious aspect of fields is dissolved. Unfortunately this has not reached a point where it can be included in this book.

Conclusion

Thus to take seriously the existence of counterspace and the ethers investigated by Steiner may provide a new basis for what underlies quantum physics. The conventional paradoxes arise because of the attempt to understand everything only in physical terms. In suggesting a new basis we are not resorting to nebulous, unquantifiable mysticism but to an aspect of the world that has its own well-defined and quantifiable laws, but is not physical. We can hope that its further development will replace the classical planetary-style reference models with something quite different. We have seen that a different way of thinking is needed to work with counterspace, indeed its very existence is posited on a different kind of consciousness. However, it is clear that what has been presented here is only a beginning. Ref. 17 provides another approach to quantum physics based on the ideas of counterspace.

18. CONCLUSION

The inclusion of counterspace in our view of the world implies a polar opposite type of agency as part of reality. We have explored the idea that objects linked to both spaces simultaneously may suffer strain, which we postulate results in stress. The stress depends upon the kind of linkage between the spaces, and simple linkages of points give rise to shift- and affine-strain and stress. The gradient of shift is generally used to secure vectors that are independent of the co-ordinates, and the analysis of this gives a coherent approach to gases, liquids and solids. A simple dualization of this (not described in the book) did not prove fruitful, which is not surprising as turn—unlike shift—is not scale-invariant. Instead the proposal was developed that for linkages involving planes the polar area of affinely linked cones expressed by bivectors results in an interesting approach to light which resolves the wave-particle duality by regarding photons instead as such linked cones. The idea that time is the reciprocal of radial turn was important for this, explaining why—as found by spiritual researchers—light has no velocity and yet at the same time why we think it does. The same idea enabled potential and force to be described. Then the concept that the ethers researched by Steiner may concern different types of time-invariance in counterspace led to the identification of the chemical ether with invariance wrt spherical surfaces and the use of surface spherical harmonics to analyse that. This brought the work close to quantum physics, and then the consideration of polarity as a strain-free transfor-mation in relation to the life ether enabled structure to be postulated for counterspaces, specifically in relation to the chemical elements. A hint as to an approach to electricity arose from that.

Chemical activity is envisaged as the bonding of elements that may arise when they relate to common spherical surfaces in which there are 'standing waves' of non-temporal turns, whereas the actual structure of the primal counterspaces seems to be governed by the life ether. The view being developed here is a non-discrete and non-particulate one in which the wave function of conventional physics seems to be concerned with the periodicities of the chemical ether. Discreteness may arise when measurements are made, but it 'evaporates' again. Thus structure seems to arise from other sources than the relationships between material particles, although we expect a high degree of correlation in view of the many experimental results of science, particularly in the realm of chemistry.

We have not, tempting as it is, imported wholesale the structure of the standard model and then merely tried to reinterpret it. This seems to be arising from the work to some extent, but it is important to develop the ideas on their own merits and see what arises. This has been the approach taken, and thus the apparent failure to jump quickly to 'obvious' further steps which has been resisted by the author.

At the end of Chapter 14 the relationship of CSIs to interactions and the collapse of the wave function was mentioned, and the possible relationship of the resulting gauge strain threshold to the self-polar surfaces of Chapter 16 is a step still being explored; it is an unfinished 'iteration' of the work to date. The relationship of time to interactions clearly requires some such step.

No attempt has yet been made to predict new observations as the total picture is not complete, and that should be accomplished first. However, it seems to be sufficiently developed to justify publication. It is the author's hope that the overall incompleteness will be seen as development potential rather than a deficiency of a theory. The work is not intended as a theory in, say, Popper's sense but rather as a possible basis for a research programme in Lakatos' sense. Perhaps this is best expressed by saying that a thought-context is justifiably demanded by science (a paradigm) and the attempt has been made to lay some foundations for such a context for a spiritual approach to science.

While it may be unfashionable in science to entertain anything non-physical, that fashion urgently needs revision when the consequences of materialism are viewed dispassionately. Penrose points to this quite clearly, albeit in more guarded terminology (Ref. 25), and Bohm was clearly of that persuasion (Ref. 6). What is quite rightly required by science is that we rely upon our own faculties to investigate the world rather than authoritative revelation, and it must be stressed again that reference to the work of Rudolf Steiner in this book is to his work as a *researcher*, not as an authoritative source. The attempt has been made to take his research seriously *as that*, and like any other research it needs to be evaluated. No request for 'special pleading' should be construed. We have followed up one important indication he gave concerning the existence of another kind of space. This can be a bridge to a spiritual view as it is quantitative, even if the quantities involved are unfamiliar. In any case they are no less strange than those used in quantum physics.

The spiritual aspect of the work lies in the role of consciousness that is implied, and the idea that force is exerted by beings rather than abstract laws. This may seem superstitious to some, but our own direct experience of force is our only justification for speaking about it at all. The strain between space and counterspace for linked objects or entities only implies stress if there are beings which suffer that stress and act to sustain what we abstractly refer to as laws. The work presented is intended to show that the idea is not mere nebulous mysticism but has quantitative aspects which give us access to such ideas in a scientific manner. That non-quantitative facets may then follow is expected, but a bridge is needed between the two so that the scientific ground given us in thought by the quantitative may be extended to the non-quantitative. This may be found when the role of thinking as a non-physical activity that underwrites the confidence we have in the quantitative is realized. Steiner's suggestion that the one area where we may experience the spirit with our ordinary faculties is the study of active thinking (Ref. 30) is again advice that can be tried out rather than a philosophy that must be believed. Physics has moved beyond materialism in this century, and it becomes important to ask what underlies the resulting mathematism if it is to relate to reality. Bohm suggested the importance of thinking at the outset in his book *Wholeness and the Implicate Order* (Ref. 6), and Steiner discovered that long before.

APPENDIX 1

TENSORS

A vector is a simple example of a tensor. Velocity is a vector, for example, the important point being that it is not affected by the co-ordinates used to describe it. The stress distribution in a strained metal bar is more complicated and may be described by a second order tensor which has nine components instead of the three describing a vector. Again the stress itself is not dependent upon the co-ordinates used. For rectangular Cartesian co-ordinates there is little problem posed by this as the components are all of the same type and there is only one type of vector, so a Euclidean transformation preserves the vector satisfactorily once it has been properly described initially. The problem is that some systems of co-ordinates have components of varied types, which makes it more difficult to relate them directly to the physical situation. For example, spherical polar co-ordinates have one length and two angles.

Tensor calculus was developed to enable physical laws to be formulated in such a way that the description is independent of the co-ordinates used. Thus an electric field varies from point to point, but the inverse square law for Coulomb attraction and repulsion does not depend upon the co-ordinates used to express it even though the electric field strength at a point is a function of the co-ordinates. If spherical polar co-ordinates are used for a point charge then we have the simplest description of its field, which is inversely proportional to the radial distance from the charge, directed along the radial line, and independent of the angles. If instead we use Cartesian co-ordinates the same behaviour must be captured by the functions of the co-ordinates used to describe the field, which are then more complicated. Is there a way of expressing this behaviour mathematically that is independent of the co-ordinates? That is the problem tensor calculus was developed to solve.

Because of the involvement of the co-ordinates in the resulting expressions the symbolism must reflect it, and so subscripts and superscripts are employed. Thus a velocity field may be described by the tensor v_i where the subscript refers to the components, v_1 being component 1 etc. Each v_i is a *function*, not merely a number, namely, a function of the co-ordinates so that those functions describe the way v_i varies in space. Thus v_i is a very *short* shorthand for a tensor as the functions may be quite complicated. The detailed development of the subject requires a study of the kinds of functions that have the required properties and the modifications necessary to carry out differentiation appropriately, which is beyond our scope. The reader may consult References such as 21 and 29 for more detail. We will, however, go a little deeper.

Work is defined as the product of the force applied and the distance through which it acts. If the force varies from point to point as in an electric field, and its line of action does not coincide with the direction of movement, then calculation becomes complicated. First of all the force must be resolved along the instantaneous direction of movement, which is accomplished by taking the inner product of the force vector and the unit vector in that direction. The result is a scalar quantity, which we would expect as work itself is a scalar, not a vector. If the force is expressed by the tensor f_i and the direction of motion by dx^i (we will see why a superscript is used shortly) then the inner product is $f_1 dx^1 + f_2 dx^2 + f_3 dx^3$ which is abbreviated as $f_i dx^i$. Einstein suggested the convention that instead of writing $\Sigma f_i dx^i$, when the symbol used for the subscript and superscript is the same (i in this case) then a summation is implied and we simply write $f_i dx^i$. Remembering that f_i and dx^i are functions we see that this means the function f_1 is multiplied by the function dx^1 and so on to obtain the inner product. Such a product is, when properly expressed, always an invariant, which is why it captures work that does not depend upon the co-ordinates. Thus $f_i dx^i$ is the tensor expression of this physical fact, an actual problem requiring the functions to be found of which f_i and dx^i are composed.

The reason for using the superscript for dx above lies in the fact that a vector may be described in two different ways when the co-ordinates are not rectangular Cartesian. One way is represented by lower indices and the other by upper ones. Figure 62 shows a vector referred to oblique co-ordinates:

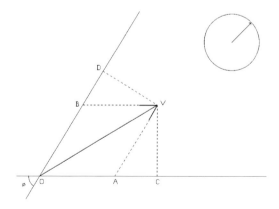

Fig. 62

We may represent the vector by its *components* (OA, OB) or by its *resolved parts* (OC, OD). If we take the inner product of the vector OV with the x direction then we multiply the resolved part OC by the displacement in the x direction. It would be wrong to multiply the component OA by that displacement. These two types of description are distinguished by writing the components with superscripts and the resolved parts with subscripts. Hence in the above example we wrote the force as f_i as we are interested in its resolved parts, whereas we wrote the displacement as dx^i because we are interested in its components. To find the inner product in an invariant manner it is necessary to use the resolved parts of one vector and the components of the other. Hence $f_i dx^i$ is invariant whereas $f_i dx_i$ and $f^i dx^i$ are not. This is essential to tensor calculus and expresses neatly the way the underlying functions are to be handled. The term *component* tends to be used for both types and the resolved parts are referred to as the *covariant components* of a vector whereas the slant components are referred to as its *contravariant components*. It must be observed, however, that the real essence of this distinction lies in how the components *vary* rather than in their relation to an origin. This is because at each point the values of the components are different and the co-ordinate directions at that point may be different, e.g. for polar co-ordinates $d\theta$ represents different directions of change for different values of θ, as is true for dr. We may refer the quantities to the x-direction by $r.\cos\theta$ to give the resolved part or covariant component, or we may use the contravariant component if we are converting to local oblique co-ordinates.

In projective geometry co-ordinates may be assigned to planes as well as points, and the condition for a point to lie in a plane is that the inner product of the co-ordinates of the two must be zero. Such an incidence relationship is an invariant fact of the geometry regardless of the co-ordinates used. Thus we may express it in tensor form by regarding the point co-ordinates as contravariant and the plane ones as covariant so that $p_i x^i = 0$ is the tensor expression of this incidence, where x^i are the homogeneous co-ordinates of the point and p_i those of the plane. This gives another view of the distinction between the types of component. However, plane co-ordinates are covariant in space but contravariant in counterspace.

If an entity varies in a more complicated way it may have two or more suffices, e.g. if it is described by functions each of which depends on two or more of the co-ordinates. For example, the way co-ordinates are converted into distances depends upon a tensor. For local oblique co-ordinates in two dimensions with an angle ϕ between the axes the distance between two neighbouring points is given by

$$ds^2 = dx^2 + dy^2 + 2.dx.dy.\cos\phi$$

which may be expressed in matrix form as

$$ds^2 = [dx \; dy] \begin{bmatrix} 1 & \cos\phi \\ \cos\phi & 1 \end{bmatrix} \begin{bmatrix} dx \\ dy \end{bmatrix}$$

The square matrix is the tensor g_{ij} called the *metric tensor* because it enables distance to be evaluated from the co-ordinates. It requires two suffices as each component is multiplied by two components of dx^i. The tensor form of this is then

$$ds^2 = g_{ij}dx^i dx^j$$

where there are two independent summations implied, one for i and one for j, which then gives the original expression for ds^2. It is a tensor equation because the distance between two points in a given space does not depend upon the co-ordinates used. The above form of g_{ij} is constant, but if ϕ is a function of position so that the angle between the local co-ordinate axes varies with position then we would have a more interesting kind of space. If $\phi = 0$ we recover Pythagoras' Theorem for rectangular co-ordinates.

The same tensor equation applies to three (or more) dimensions, the difference being that the suffices range from 1 to 3 instead of 1 to 2.

The expression $g_{ij}dx^i dx^j$ is a quadratic form, and in terms of group theory the *orthogonal group* leaves such a quadratic form invariant.

Tensors are used in physics to express physical laws in their most essential form, independent of the co-ordinates. A formulation of a law that does depend upon the co-ordinates is necessarily suspect as nature can hardly be expected to depend upon how we choose to describe her. A notorious example lay in the behaviour of pendulums in the presence of acceleration. It seemed that it was necessary to choose a reference system that was in uniform rectilinear motion in order to frame such laws correctly. Einstein's General Theory of Relativity was formulated to solve this problem, which required that it be impossible to distinguish experimentally between the presence of a gravitational field and a state of acceleration. That in turn requires the principle of equivalence, that inertial and gravitational mass are indistinguishable. It would scarcely be possible to express the laws of physics in such a way that they are invariant under the wide class of transformations implied (Riemannian transformations) without the use of tensor calculus.

We have described tensors in terms of physical entities, but in fact several distinct tensors may relate to one underlying physical entity, so strictly speaking a tensor is a mathematical entity. However it is easier to grasp their import initially by referring to invariant physical entities.

APPENDIX 2

COUNTERSPACE MATHEMATICS

In this appendix we establish some basic concepts and mathematical results for general use.

Orthogonality

Two points are orthogonal if they lie on orthogonal lines through O.

In the projective interpretation of Euclidean space two coplanar lines are orthogonal if they intersect the plane at infinity Ω in two conjugate points wrt the absolute circle. Dually two concurrent lines in counterspace are orthogonal if the two planes they determine in O are conjugate wrt the absolute cone, which means they are orthogonal in the customary Euclidean sense.

We often need to calculate turns, and a useful relation is provided by its appearance as the parameter of an axial pencil. First we will briefly introduce plane co-ordinates.

Plane Co-ordinates

If a point lies in a plane then it satisfies a linear equation of the form

$$x_0 u_0 + x_1 u_1 + x_2 u_2 + x_3 u_3 = 0$$

where the x_i are the homogeneous co-ordinates of the point and the u_i are constants. In vector notation this is $\mathbf{x}.\mathbf{u} = 0$. Any values of the x_i which satisfy this (apart from $x_i = 0$ for all i) specify a point in a plane determined by the constants u_i. If we change the values of the u_i then we change the plane in which the points lie. We could thus regard the u_i also as being variable, and if now we take a fixed point x_i and vary the u_i instead we obtain all the possible planes that contain x_i, i.e. a bundle of planes. Thus the above equation is symmetrical, which expresses algebraically the principle of duality between points and planes, and we can regard the u_i as *co-ordinates of planes* with as much justification as we regard the x_i as co-ordinates of points. If $x_1 = x_2 = 0$ and $x_3 = u_3 = 1$ then $x_0 = -1/u_0$, i.e. the plane intersects the x-axis at a distance $-1/u_0$ from the origin, or more generally at $-u_3/u_0$, which gives a feel for the meaning of the co-ordinates. It also shows a relationship to the definition of turn.

The co-ordinate planes have the co-ordinates $(0,0,0,1)$, $(1,0,0,0)$, $(0,1,0,0)$ and $(0,0,1,0)$ so that, for example, points in the XY plane have $x_2 = 0$ so $(0,0,1,0)$ is that plane, which satisfies the above equation for all its points.

A quadratic equation in plane co-ordinates represents a quadric surface in terms of its tangent planes, e.g. $u_0^2 + u_1^2 - u_3^2 = 0$ is a cone.

If we consider $u_i + \mu v_i \equiv \mathbf{u} + \mu \mathbf{v}$ where $\mathbf{u}, \mathbf{v}$ are two fixed planes and μ is a parameter, then clearly it represents a set of planes as μ varies. A point $\mathbf{x}$ lying in both $\mathbf{u}$ and $\mathbf{v}$ is such that $\mathbf{x}.\mathbf{u} = 0$ and $\mathbf{x}.\mathbf{v} = 0$, so $\mathbf{x}.(\mathbf{u} + \mu \mathbf{v}) = 0$ and thus $\mathbf{x}$ lies in all the planes of the set. Thus all the points on the line common to $\mathbf{u}$ and $\mathbf{v}$ lie in all the planes of the set, and we see that $u_i + \mu v_i$ represents the axial pencil of planes in that line.

Turn Between Planes

Figure 63 shows a line through O and two planes α, β of an axial pencil orthogonal to the page with its axis orthogonal to P. If P has the

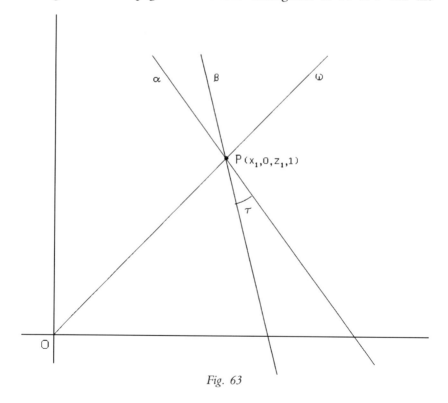

Fig. 63

homogeneous co-ordinates $(x_1, 0, z_1, 1)$, assuming the y-axis is orthogonal to the page, then α has the plane co-ordinates $(az_1, 0, -1 - ax_1, z_1)$ since the inner product of α with P must be zero, as is that with the point at infinity $I = (0, 1, 0, 0)$ on the y-axis. Similarly $\beta = (bz_1, 0, -1 - bx_1, z_1)$, which shows that a general plane of the pencil has the co-ordinates $(\mu z_1, 0, -1 - \mu x_1, z_1)$ where μ is the parameter of the pencil. When $\mu = \infty$ we have the plane w of the pencil containing O with co-ordinates $(z_1, 0, -x_1, 0)$. Regarding β as a variable plane we now express the pencil as $b = \alpha + \nu w$ with parameter ν, i.e.

$$\{bz_1, 0, -1 - bx_1, z_1\} = \{az_1, 0, -1 - ax_1, z_1\} + \{\nu z_1, 0, -\nu x_1, 0\}$$
$$= \{(a + \nu)z_1, 0, -1 - (a + \nu)x_1, z_1\}$$

so

$$\nu = b - a$$

If we substitute the co-ordinates of α and β in the expression

$$\tau^2 = \frac{(u_0 v_3 - v_0 u_3)^2 + (u_1 v_3 - v_1 u_3)^2 + (u_2 v_3 - v_2 u_3)^2}{u_3^2 v_3^2}$$

for the turn between two planes, the turn τ is given by

$$\tau^2 = \frac{(bz_1^2 - az_1^2)^2 + 0 + (ax_1 z_1 - bx_1 z_1)^2}{z_1^2}$$
$$= (b - a)^2 (z_1^2 + x_1^2)$$

If we normalize w to have a modulus of 1 so that $(z_1^2 + x_1^2) = 1$ (this does not affect P as here we are merely using the ratio $x_1 : z_1$ for w) we see that $\tau = \nu$, i.e. the parameter of the axial pencil is then the turn from α to β. Thus

> **Given any two planes α, β with known co-ordinates, we simply find the normalized co-ordinates of the plane w in O and their common line, and find the turn τ between them from the relation $\beta = \alpha + \tau w$.**

Note that $\alpha_3 = \beta_3 = 1$ for this to be correct. The sign of τ is a matter of convention depending upon the application, for we may take $w_i = -w_i$ and thus reverse it (as the co-ordinates are homogeneous).

Shift Between Lines

In space there is an angle between two coplanar lines, and in counterspace there is a shift between two concurrent lines. If the two lines intersect Ω in two points A, B and the line AB intersects the absolute circle in the (imaginary) points I, J then the angle is given by Cayley's formula involving the cross-ratio (AB, IJ)

$$\frac{\log\{(AB, IJ)\}}{2i}$$

Dually two concurrent lines in counterspace determine two planes α, β in O, and the line (α, β) contains two (imaginary) tangent planes ν, η to the absolute cone so that the shift is the above formula applied to the cross-ratio $(\alpha\beta, \nu\eta)$. The result is identical to the Euclidean angle between the planes α and β, for the same configuration regarded as lying in space would define the angle between those planes.

Summarizing, the shift between two lines in counterspace is the angle between the planes they subtend in O.

Turn Between Any Two Planes and the Cosine Rule

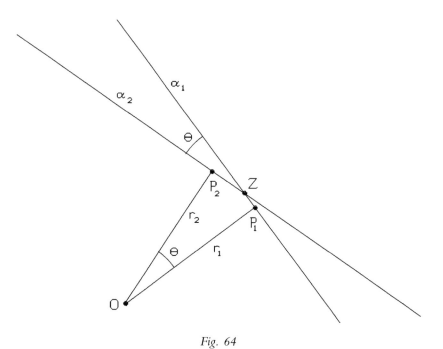

Fig. 64

Given two planes α_1, α_2 orthogonal to the diagram as shown and the vectors (r_i, θ_i) orthogonal to them, the shift between them is $(\theta_2 - \theta_1)$. The α_i have the plane co-ordinates

$$\left\{ \frac{-\cos\left(\theta_i\right)}{r_i}, -\frac{\sin\left(\theta_i\right)}{r_i}, 0, 1 \right\} \tag{1}$$

which is easily verified by taking the inner product with the point co-ordinates $(r_i \cos\theta_i, r_i \sin\theta_i, 0, 1)$ of the points P_i. If the point Z has co-ordinates $(x, y, \xi, 1)$ where x and y are determined by α_1 and α_2 while ξ is a parameter for all points on the line, then x and y satisfy

$$-x\cos\theta_1 - y\sin\theta_1 + r_1 = 0$$
$$-x\cos\theta_2 - y\sin\theta_2 + r_2 = 0$$

and solving gives

$$x = \frac{r_2 \sin\theta_1 - r_1 \sin\theta_2}{\sin\left(\theta_1 - \theta_2\right)}$$

$$y = \frac{r_1 \cos\theta_2 - r_2 \cos\theta_1}{\sin\left(\theta_1 - \theta_2\right)}$$

Now the plane η through the line (α_1, α_2) containing Z has the co-ordinates $(y, -x, 0, 0)$ which in normalized form are

$$\left[\frac{y}{\sqrt{x^2 + y^2}}, -\frac{x}{\sqrt{x^2 + y^2}}, 0, 0 \right]$$

Substituting for x and y from the above expressions and simplifying gives the unit infinite plane as

$$\left[\frac{r_1 \cos\theta_2 - r_2 \cos\theta_1}{\sqrt{r_1^2 + r_2^2 - 2r_1 r_2 \cos\left(\theta_1 - \theta_2\right)}}, \frac{r_1 \sin\theta_2 - r_2 \sin\theta_1}{\sqrt{r_1^2 + r_2^2 - 2r_1 r_2 \cos\left(\theta_1 - \theta_2\right)}}, 0, 0 \right] \tag{2}$$

Now a variable plane β about a line in the plane α_1 is $\beta = \alpha_1 + \rho\eta$ where η is the normalized infinite plane in the line and ρ is the magnitude of the turn. Thus $\alpha_2 = \alpha_1 + \rho\eta$, which from (1) and (2) above is

$$\left(\frac{-\cos\theta_1}{r_1}, \frac{-\sin\theta_1}{r_1}, 0, 1 \right)$$

$$+\rho \left[\frac{r_1 \cos\theta_2 - r_2 \cos\theta_1}{\sqrt{r_1^2 + r_2^2 - 2r_1 r_2 \cos\left(\theta_1 - \theta_2\right)}}, \frac{r_1 \sin\theta_2 - r_2 \sin\theta_1}{\sqrt{r_1^2 + r_2^2 - 2r_1 r_2 \cos\left(\theta_1 - \theta_2\right)}}, 0, 0 \right]$$

This equals expression (1) applied to α_2, so equating expressions for x we find

$$\rho \frac{r_1 \cos\theta_2 - r_2 \cos\theta_1}{\sqrt{r_1^2 + r_2^2 - 2r_1 r_2 \cos\left(\theta_1 - \theta_2\right)}} - \frac{\cos\theta_1}{r_1} = -\frac{\cos\theta_2}{r_2}$$

Hence we find, taking the positive value, that the turn from α_1 to α_2 is

$$\rho = \frac{\sqrt{r_1^2 + r_2^2 - 2r_1 r_2 \cos(\theta_1 - \theta_2)}}{r_1 r_2}$$

We get the same result by equating expressions for y. If we replace r_1 and r_2 by $\rho_1 = 1/r_1$ and $\rho_2 = 1/r_2$, i.e. by the turns in from infinity, the above equation becomes

$$\rho = \sqrt{\rho_1^2 + \rho_2^2 - 2\rho_1 \rho_2 \cos(\theta_1 - \theta_2)}$$

which is the cosine rule for the counterspace triangle $\alpha_1 \alpha_2 \Omega$, $(\theta_1 - \theta_2) = \theta$ being the shift between the lines $(\alpha_1 \Omega)$ and $(\alpha_2 \Omega)$, noting that the planes they subtend in O are Euclideanly parallel to the planes α_1 and α_2 and hence include the same angle θ. We must stress that we are using angles as a convenient way of handling shifts, and that in pure counterspace only the shifts are significant.

APPENDIX 3

VECTORS IN COUNTERSPACE

Vector algebra is identical for counterspace since the same algebra applies to plane co-ordinates as to point co-ordinates. However, it is valuable to see how to visualize what this means in order to get a feel for the subject, as aspects run counter to our Euclidean spatial intuition. In particular we will see how to resolve vectors, as the analysis of a vector into its radial and tangential components is needed.

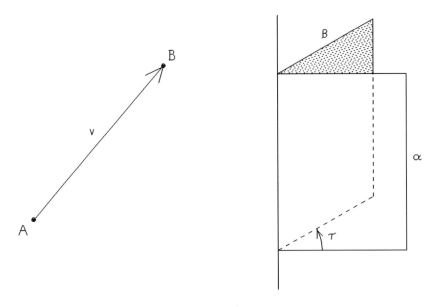

Fig. 65

A vector has a magnitude v and a direction represented by a line AB of length v as shown in Fig. 65 on the left. The quantity represented by the vector, e.g. the strength of an electric field, is located at A and acts in the direction shown, but it does not 'extend' to B; the arrow is purely representational. A counterspace vector has a magnitude expressed by a turn, dual to the use of a length to express a spatial one. On the right we show the dual representation of a counterspace vector which is at the plane α and acts about the vertical line shown, the plane β playing the same representational role as B to indicate the magnitude τ of the turn.

We will now see how to resolve such a vector in the radial and tangential directions.

At the top left of Fig. 66 we show the spatial resolution of a vector v into its radial component r and its tangential component t. The large diagram shows planes represented by lines, so that the point A in the spatial diagram has its dual as the plane A represented by the horizontal line labelled A. The spatial vector v is represented by the line AB which is dualized as the turn τ between the planes A and B as shown. The line of action v is dualized as the line orthogonal to the diagram at the point marked v where the lines representing the planes A and B meet. The component r of the spatial vector in the radial direction passes through the centre O of the sphere, so dually the line of action r of the counterspace radial component lies in the centre plane Ω, i.e. is at infinity as indicated. To find the spatial magnitude we draw the line $\underline{a}$ orthogonal to r, or BC orthogonal to OA, giving the point C. To dualize this we must see what orthogonal means in counterspace.

Two lines in space are orthogonal if they meet the plane at infinity in two points which are conjugate wrt the absolute circle, and the dual in counterspace is that two lines are orthogonal if their 'planes at infinity' are

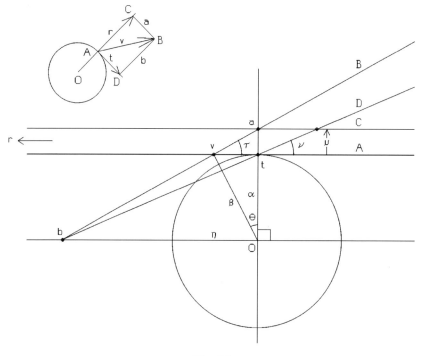

Fig. 66

conjugate wrt the absolute cone of counterspace, i.e. if the planes through those lines containing O are conjugate. Euclideanly speaking this means that their planes containing O are orthogonal, which in pure counterspace terminology means that any point on one line has a shift of 90° wrt any point on the other. This is true if the planes are orthogonal in the Euclidean sense.

Returning to the construction of the line a orthogonal to r, the plane η through O and r is shown parallel to A, so a must lie in the plane α through O orthogonal to that, as shown. Since a lies in the plane B we see that it is the line where α and B intersect. Then we find the plane C dual to the point C as the plane common to a and r, which is shown parallel to A. Thus the component of τ in the radial direction is the turn μ between the planes A and C.

Now we need to find the component t. In space t contains A and is orthogonal to OA, so in counterspace t lies in the planes α and A represented by the point t shown. To find the point D in space we draw the line b parallel to r meeting AD in D, so dually b is the line where η and B meet. The point D in space is the meet of the lines b and t, so in counterspace it is the plane D containing b and t. The tangential component of τ is thus the turn ν between the planes A and D, and we have completed the process.

In space we complete a parallelogram in the general case, and the parallelogram in counterspace is composed of the lines r, t, a, b on the two orthogonal planes η and α. They contain a common point at infinity as they are all parallel which is dual to the common plane of the lines r, t, a, b in space containing O. The line v also contains that point as it should.

What makes the turn ν a tangential one is not as obvious intuitively as the fact that μ is radial. Observe that its line of action t is located in the plane α through O orthogonal to the base plane A of the vector. It is *this* condition that makes it tangential. This is illustrated by the fact that application of the above process to this vector results in a zero radial component.

We have given the example of finding the radial and tangential components of a vector as it is has important applications, and we will now generalize the procedure for finding the components of a counterspace vector. Generally we may choose any two directions in the base point A of a spatial vector along which we will resolve it, provided they determine a plane containing the vector. In counterspace we may thus choose any two lines of action provided they lie in the base plane of the vector (as r and t did above) and meet on the line common to A and B (dual to r, t and v lying in a plane), and then complete the counterspace parallelogram (see Fig. 67). If these two lines are a and b, then they meet in some point P which is the dual of the plane of the parallelogam. They determine two planes α, β in O which contain lines of counterspace parallel to them, and hence contain the opposite sides c, d of the parallelogram. Since the latter contain the plane B of the turn $\tau = (AB)$, the lines c and d are the intercepts of B with α and β. This must needs be drawn in three dimensions:

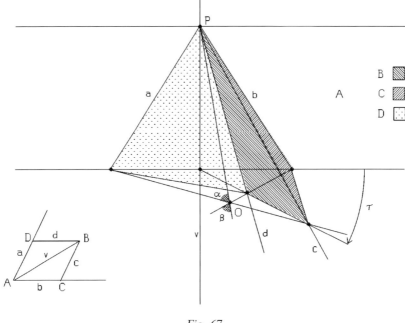

Fig. 67

The components of the vector are the turns between A and $C = (bc)$ and A and $D = (ad)$. This shows the parallelogram construction in the general case. We see that if we choose the plane through O orthogonal to A then the construction of the points to be joined to P to give the solution is very simple (Fig. 68).

The diagram shows the base plane A, represented by a line, which is orthogonal to the plane of the diagram through O, the plane B of the vector, and the points where the lines a and b intersect the diagram. We draw the lines joining a and b to O which then intersect B in the points c and d. This gives the turns of the components ν and μ between A and (ad) and A and (bc) respectively. μ looks too large in this diagram, but it should be borne in mind that the actual turns between the planes involved depend upon the three-dimensional situation. The previous diagram is then recovered by joining a, b, c, d to P.

We also need to see how to resolve a vector along a general direction, i.e. to find its inner product with a unit turn in that direction.

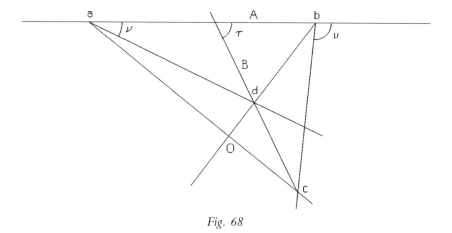

Fig. 68

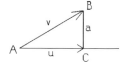

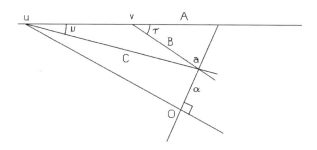

Fig. 69

The line of action u of the unit turn must again lie in the base plane A, and we find the plane α containing lines orthogonal in counterspace to u as the plane through O orthogonal to the plane (Ou). Then the line a in B orthogonal to u is the line where α intersects B. We join u and a to give the plane C, yielding the resolved turn μ as shown.

In affine geometry the concept 'orthogonal' does not exist and so we cannot find the resolved parts of vectors, only their components, as the latter depend upon the concept of parallelism but not orthogonality. We used orthogonality to find the radial and tangential components. However, reviewing again Fig. 66 above we note that given a tangent plane A the line r is the line at infinity in it, the line t is that line in A parallel to v which touches the sphere, and then α is the plane through t and O. Hence we can find α in the affine case, and the rest of the construction stands as it is without recourse to orthogonality.

Gauss's Theorem

In vector analysis a very useful theorem which we will need is Gauss's Theorem which states that

$$\int_s \tau.\mathbf{ds} = \int_v \nabla.\tau\mathrm{dv}$$

This says that given a closed surface and a vector field τ, the surface integral of the inner product of the vector at a point with the surface element at that point equals the volume integral of the divergence of the field. It is thus very useful for relating what is happening on a surface to what is happening inside it, and a typical application is to electric fields where the enclosed charge is measured by the divergence and the total flux normal to the surface by the surface integral. The point is that the latter is independent of the shape of the surface provided the same charge is enclosed.

For counterspace τ will be a field of turns and so the inner product is taken of a turn vector at a tangent plane with the surface element, the latter being the point of tangency (dual to the planar surface element in space). The divergence is non-zero if there are sources or sinks in the field enclosed by the polar volume (i.e. outside the surface spatially speaking). In space divergence occurs at a point, while in counterspace it occurs at a plane. A purely radial field in space has spherical surfaces of equal potential centred on the point of divergence, and dually in counterspace such a field has equipotential surfaces which appear in space as prolate spheroids and hyperboloids with the CSI at one focus and the centre plane polar to the other (which is a focal plane in counterspace). The centre plane is the plane of divergence.

A charge distribution also gives rise to divergence, e.g. in a volume or surface. In this sense a circular area in space and dually a cone in counterspace can give rise to divergence.

Analytic Approach

To use Gauss's Theorem and other vector methods effectively we need a more convenient way of handling vectors analytically. As plane co-ordinates are little used now, we will demonstrate the validity of their use for counterspace vectors in a polar fashion. Having seen pictorially how to resolve vectors so that we have a feel for what is involved, we will now derive the plane co-ordinate approach from our definition of turn as the parameter of an axial pencil.

In Fig. 66 we will derive the expressions for τ, μ and ν. For τ we have

$$B_i = A_i + \tau \beta_i \tag{1}$$

denoting the plane co-ordinates of B by B_i etc., and noting that β_i is a unit vector. We need the co-ordinates of β_i, which are evidently

$$\beta_i = \frac{B_i - A_i}{\sqrt{\sum_0^2 (B_i - A_i)^2}} \tag{2}$$

which is a unit vector with the fourth co-ordinate zero, which is why the summation to give the magnitude is from 0 to 2 instead of 0 to 3. As we are working metrically we set the fourth co-ordinates of all vectors such as A_i to 1 to yield correct values for the turns.

With no loss of generality we may ease the work by taking the third co-ordinate as zero since all the planes in Fig. 66 are orthogonal to the diagram. Note also that the fourth co-ordinates of α_i, β_i and η_i are zero as they contain O.

Next we note that A_i and α_i are orthogonal, so that $\mathbf{A}.\alpha = 0$, i.e.

$$A_0 \alpha_0 + A_1 \alpha_1 = 0$$

so that

$$\alpha = \left\{ \frac{-A_1}{\sqrt{A}}, \frac{A_0}{\sqrt{A}}, 0, 0 \right\} \tag{3}$$

where for economy we write $\sqrt{A} = \sqrt{A_0^2 + A_1^2}$.

Consider now the plane C_i. It is parallel to A_i and thus satisfies the parametric equation

$$C_i = A_i + \omega \Omega_i$$

and since $\Omega_i = \{0, 0, 0, 1\}$ clearly $\mathbf{C} = \{A_0, A_1, A_2, 1 + \omega\}$, which must be normalized by dividing all co-ordinates by $1 + \omega$. Thus parallel planes have their first three co-ordinates in the same ratio. Thus we deduce that the plane η_i which is parallel to A_i is

$$\eta = \left\{ \frac{A_0}{\sqrt{A}}, \frac{A_1}{\sqrt{A}}, 0, 0 \right\} \tag{4}$$

The turn τ is now given by (1) which gives using (2)

$$\{B_0, B_1, 0, 1\} = \left\{A_0 + \frac{\tau(B_0 - A_0)}{\sqrt{B - A}}, \ A_1 + \frac{\tau(B_1 - A_1)}{\sqrt{B - A}}, \ 0, 1\right\}$$

Clearly the solution is $\tau = \sqrt{b - A}$, i.e.

$$\tau = \sqrt{(B_0 - A_0)^2 + (B_1 - A_1)^2} \tag{5}$$

which is a familiar form in vector terms, showing that turns relate to plane co-ordinates just as points do to point co-ordinates.

Using (4) the radial component μ of τ is given by

$$C_i = A_i + \mu \eta_i - \left\{A_0 + \frac{\mu A_0}{\sqrt{A}}, \ A_1 + \frac{\mu A_1}{\sqrt{A}}, 0, 1\right\} \tag{6}$$

To specify C_i fully we also note that it forms an axial pencil with B_i and α_i and thus satisfies

$$C_i = B_i + \omega \alpha_i$$

for some value of ω. taking care with signs. Hence using (3)

$$C_i = \left\{B_0 - \frac{\omega A_1}{\sqrt{A}}, \ B_1 + \frac{\omega A_0}{\sqrt{A}}, 0, 1\right\}$$

and comparing this with (6) we must equate the expressions for C_0 and C_1 which on eliminating ω from the two resulting equations gives

$$\mu = -\sqrt{A} \ \frac{A_0 B_0 + A_1 B_1}{\sqrt{A}} \tag{7}$$

To find the tangential component ν of τ we note that D_i belongs firstly to the pencil given by B_i and η_i, and secondly to that given by A_i and α_i. Using the same methods as above and solving the equations

$$D_i = B_i + \sigma \eta_i$$
$$D_i = A_i + \nu \alpha_i$$

for ν by eliminating σ we get

$$\nu = \frac{A_0 B_1 - A_1 B_0}{\sqrt{A}} \tag{8}$$

We should find that $\tau^2 = \mu^2 + \nu^2$, which is easily verified from (5),(7) and (8).

The vector expressed by the turn between A_i and B_i is $v_i = B_i - A_i$, which from (5) we have seen has a conventional vector magnitude in terms of its first three plane co-ordinates, equal to the turn τ between B_i and A_i.

The first three plane (homogeneous) co-ordinates form the polar-Euclidean co-ordinates when the fourth co-ordinate is unity, which we have assumed. Then $\sqrt{A}$, which omits the fourth co-ordinate, is the proper magnitude of the polar-Euclidean vector. We may now re-express (7) for μ as

$$\mu = \frac{\mathbf{A}.(\mathbf{B} - \mathbf{A})}{\sqrt{\mathbf{A}.\mathbf{A}}} = \frac{\mathbf{A}.\mathbf{v}}{\sqrt{\mathbf{A}.\mathbf{A}}} = \hat{\mathbf{A}}.\mathbf{v}$$

where $\hat{\mathbf{A}}$ is the unit vector in the direction of $\mathbf{A}$. Similarly we find that

$$\nu = |\hat{\mathbf{A}} \times \mathbf{B}| = |\hat{\mathbf{A}} \times (\mathbf{B} - \mathbf{A})| = |\hat{\mathbf{A}} \times \mathbf{v}|$$
$$\tau = \sqrt{\mathbf{v}.\mathbf{v}}$$

which are exactly dual to the expressions for conventional spatial vectors, as illustrated in Fig. 70:

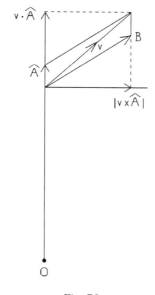

Fig. 70

Clearly the above work may be generalized for third co-ordinates not equal to zero, by redefining $\sqrt{A} = \sqrt{A_0^2 + A_1^2 + A_2^2}$ etc. and including the extra terms in all expressions.

Thus for a vector $\mathbf{v}$ on a surface we find its radial component by taking its inner product with the unit vector corresponding to the base plane taken as a tangent plane to a sphere centred on O, and its tangential component by taking the outer product.

The Euclidean angle θ between the planes α and β is given by $\alpha.\beta$ which using (2), (3), (5) and (8) is

$$\cos(\theta) = \frac{-A_1(B_0 - A_0)}{\sqrt{A}\sqrt{B-A}} + \frac{A_0(B_1 - A_1)}{\sqrt{A}\sqrt{B-A}} = \frac{A_0 B_1 - A_1 B_0}{\sqrt{A}\sqrt{B-A}} = \frac{\nu}{\tau}$$

and similarly $\sin(\theta) = \mu/\tau$ so that $\mu = \tau.\sin(\theta)$ and $\nu = \tau.\cos(\theta)$ as in conventional vector algebra. θ can of course be reinterpreted as a shift. It is the angle joining O to the line of action and that through O normal to the base plane and parallel to the line of action.

APPENDIX 4

CHORD LAW OF SHIFT STRAIN

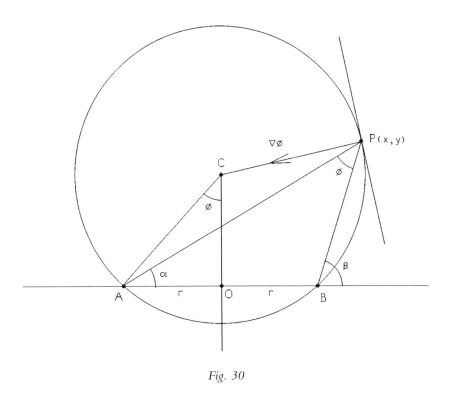

Fig. 30

Figure 30 shows two CSIs at A and B and a point P with shift strain ϕ wrt the CSIs. We will calculate the gradient of the strain. From inspection we see that ϕ is constant if P moves round the circle, so we expect $\nabla\phi$ to be in the direction orthogonal to the tangent at P. The gradient as a vector is

$$\left(\frac{\partial\phi}{\partial x}, \frac{\partial\phi}{\partial y}\right)$$

Now $\phi = \beta - \alpha$, so

$$\frac{\partial\phi}{\partial y} = \frac{\partial\beta}{\partial y} - \frac{\partial\alpha}{\partial y}$$

and since

$$\tan\beta = \frac{y}{x-r}$$

we have

$$\sec^2\beta.\frac{\partial\beta}{\partial y} = \frac{1}{x-r}$$

giving, as $\sec^2(\beta) = 1 + \tan^2(\beta)$,

$$\frac{\partial\beta}{\partial y} = \frac{1}{(x-r)\left(1 + \frac{y^2}{(x-r)^2}\right)}$$

i.e.

$$\frac{\partial\beta}{\partial y} = \frac{x-r}{(x-r)^2 + y^2}$$

Similarly

$$\frac{\partial\alpha}{\partial y} = \frac{x+r}{(x+r)^2 + y^2}$$

so

$$\frac{\partial\phi}{\partial y} = \frac{\{(x+r)^2 + y^2\}(x-r) - \{(x-r)^2 + y^2\}(x+r)}{\{(x+r)^2 + y^2\}\{(x-r)^2 + y^2\}}$$

which simplifies to

$$\frac{\partial\phi}{\partial y} = \frac{2r(x^2 - y^2 - r^2)}{(x^2 + y^2 + r^2)^2 - 4r^2x^2}$$

Similarly

$$\frac{\partial\beta}{\partial x} = \frac{-y}{(x-r)^2 + y^2}$$

and

$$\frac{\partial\alpha}{\partial x} = \frac{-y}{(x+r)^2 + y^2}$$

so

$$\frac{\partial\phi}{\partial x} = \frac{-y\{(x+r)^2 + y^2 - (x-r)^2 - y^2}{\{(x+r)^2 + y^2\}\{(x-r)^2 + y^2\}}$$

i.e.

$$\frac{\partial \phi}{\partial x} = \frac{-4rxy}{(x^2 + y^2 + r^2)^2 - 4r^2 x^2} = \frac{-4rxy}{D}$$

The amplitude of $\nabla \phi$ is thus

$$|\nabla \phi| = \sqrt{\left(\frac{\partial \phi}{\partial x}\right)^2 + \left(\frac{\partial \phi}{\partial y}\right)^2} = 2r\sqrt{\frac{4x^2 y^2 + x^4 + y^4 + r^4 - 2x^2 y^2 - 2x^2 r^2 + 2y^2 r^2}{D}}$$

$$= \frac{2r\sqrt{D}}{D}$$

$$= \frac{2r}{\sqrt{D}} \tag{1}$$

To obtain the direction θ of $\nabla \phi$ we have

$$\tan \theta = \frac{\partial \phi / \partial y}{\partial \phi / \partial x} = \frac{2r(x^2 - y^2 - r^2)}{-4rxy} = m$$

This direction is along a straight line through P with this gradient, so its equation is $Y = mX + c$, giving for $Y = y$ and $X = x$

$$c = \frac{x^2 + y^2 - r^2}{2y}$$

and thus when $X = 0$ we have

$$Y = \frac{x^2 + y^2 - r^2}{2y}$$

Now the centre of the circle C subtends an angle ϕ as shown in the diagram, so

$$\mathrm{OC} = \frac{r}{\tan \phi}$$

and

$$\tan \phi = \frac{\tan \beta - \tan \alpha}{1 + \tan \beta \tan \alpha} = \frac{\dfrac{y}{x - r} - \dfrac{y}{x + r}}{1 + \dfrac{y^2}{x^2 - r^2}} = \frac{2yr}{x^2 + y^2 - r^2}$$

whence it is clear that $\mathrm{OC} = Y$, i.e. the line of the gradient passes through the centre of the circle as we saw initially from the geometry. From the signs of $\partial \phi / \partial y$ and $\partial \phi / \partial x$ it is also clear that the gradient is directed inwards. Thus the rate of change of strain increases inwardly, and decreases outwardly. The field lines generated by this gradient are the Apollonian circles orthogonal to the Steiner circles in A and B.

If we let $AP = 2s$ and $BP = 2t$ (analogously to $AB = 2r$) then $D = 16s^2t^2$ so from (1) we have

$$|\nabla\phi| = \frac{r}{2st}$$

If we redefine r, s, t as $r = AB$, $s = AP$ and $t = BP$ then this becomes

$$|\nabla\phi| = \frac{r}{st}$$

which shows an interesting symmetry. If we let $\phi = \phi_B$, then we have

$$|\nabla\phi_B| = \frac{s}{rt} \text{ where } \phi_B = 180 - \beta$$

and

$$|\nabla\phi_A| = \frac{t}{rs}$$

This gives a concise description of three interacting CSIs: the gradients of the strain all act inwardly along radii of their circumcircle with magnitudes related to the chords as above. As the rate of change of strain is relieved by outward movement, their reaction to that will be in the direction opposite to the gradient. If the stress acts thus, then since $\nabla\phi$ acts along radii there is no resultant turning moment. However there is a resultant stress (i.e. the three are not in equilibrium), which is most clear if ABP is a right-angled triangle as then two of the stresses act oppositely along the hypotenuse, and there is obviously a resultant stress. This has the interesting corollary that should such a stress situation be realized in practice, and should the three CSIs be rigidly linked, then the total configuration will move of itself, unlike normal force configurations. Otherwise three such CSIs will move into equilibrium since the stress will be greatest on the closest pair, evolving the triangle towards an equilateral one.

For ease of reference we will refer to the above result as the

Chord Law
If three CSIs interact through shift strain, then referring to their common circle, the magnitude of the strain gradient at a CSI equals the opposite chord over the product of the adjacent chords, directed towards the centre of the circle.

This gives a clear insight into how the magnitude varies. If one CSI moves away from the other two then one chord stays fixed while the other two increase. The latter are the denominator chords, and so when they are much greater than the fixed chord we have the inverse square law approximately for the moving CSI, while the remaining two see virtually no change. However, if the three separate so that the triangle remains equilateral then we have an inverse first power law for all three.

APPENDIX 5

AFFINE STRAIN IN LIQUIDS

This appendix will derive in detail the results quoted in Chapter 10. We will analyse the shift strain acting on one vertex of a constant-volume tetrahedron.

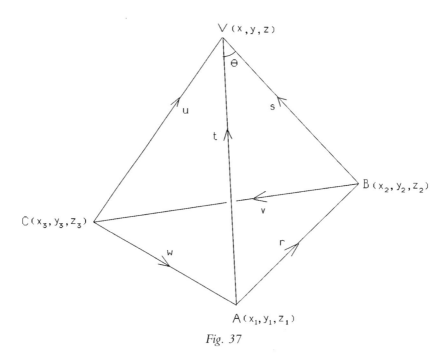

Fig. 37

Figure 37 shows a tetrahedron with sides as vectors, and vertices with their appropriate co-ordinates. For the angle θ shown we have

$$\cos \theta = \frac{\mathbf{s.t}}{st}$$

so

$$- \sin \theta \, \frac{\partial \theta}{\partial x} = \frac{st\left(s_{x'} \, t_x + t_{x'} s_x\right) - \mathbf{s.t}\left(s't + t's\right)}{s^2 t^2}$$

$$= \frac{s_{x'} t_x + t_{x'} s_x}{st} - \frac{\mathbf{s.t.}\left(\dfrac{s_x s_{x'} t}{s} + \dfrac{t_x t_{x'} s}{t}\right)}{s^2 t^2}$$

noting

$$s = \sqrt{s_x^2 + s_y^2 + s_z^2}$$

where $'$ denotes differentiation wrt $\mathbf{x}$, bold type denotes a vector, and s_x is the x-component of $\mathbf{s}$ etc.

We adopt the convention that $t_x = x - x_1$, $s_x = x - x_2$ etc. where

$$V = \{x, y, z\}$$
$$A = \{x_1, y_1, z_1\}$$
$$B = \{x_2, y_2, z_2\}$$
$$C = \{x_3, y_3, z_3\}$$

Then $s_x' = t_x' = 1$. Noting further that $s.t.\sin\theta = $ twice the area of triangle ABV, say A_1, we have

$$-2A_1 \frac{\partial\theta}{\partial x} = s_x + t_x - \mathbf{s.t}\left(\frac{s_x}{s^2} + \frac{t_x}{t^2}\right)$$

$$= s_x\left(1 - \frac{\mathbf{s.t}}{s^2}\right) + t_x\left(1 - \frac{\mathbf{s.t}}{t^2}\right)$$

Now

$$1 - \frac{\mathbf{s.t}}{s^2} = \frac{s_x^2 + s_y^2 + s_z^2 - s_x t_x - s_y t_y - s_z t_z}{s^2}$$

$$= \frac{s_x(s_x - t_x) + s_y(s_y - t_y) + s_z(s_z - t_z)}{s^2}$$

$$= -\frac{\mathbf{s.r}}{s^2} \quad (\mathbf{r} \text{ directed as shown})$$

Similarly $\quad 1 - \dfrac{\mathbf{s.t}}{t^2} = +\dfrac{\mathbf{t.r}}{t^2}$

so

$$2A_1 \frac{\partial\theta}{\partial x} = \frac{s_x \mathbf{s.r}}{s^2} - \frac{t_x \mathbf{t.r}}{t^2} \tag{3}$$

Repeating for the other two triangles VBC and VCA and adding the three results (as they are all scalars in the x-direction) we have

$$2(A_1 + A_2 + A_3)\frac{\partial\theta}{\partial x} = \frac{s_x \mathbf{s.r}}{s^2} - \frac{t_x \mathbf{t.r}}{t^2} + \frac{u_x \mathbf{u.v}}{u^2} - \frac{s_x \mathbf{s.v}}{s^2} + \frac{t_x \mathbf{t.w}}{t^2} - \frac{u_x \mathbf{u.w}}{u^2}$$

$$= \frac{s_x \mathbf{s.}(\mathbf{r} - \mathbf{v})}{s^2} + \frac{t_x \mathbf{t.}(\mathbf{w} - \mathbf{r})}{t^2} + \frac{u_x \mathbf{u.}(\mathbf{v} - \mathbf{w})}{u^2}$$

$$= s_x l + t_x m + u_x n$$

where l, m, n are defined accordingly.

Hence

$$\frac{\partial \theta}{\partial x} = \frac{s_x l + t_x m + u_x n}{2(A_1 + A_2 + A_3)}$$

Since l, m, n are independent of the co-ordinates we see that partial differentiation wrt y gives the same result, except that the x suffices are replaced by y suffices, and similarly for z.

Evidently we may combine the x, y and z components to give us the total gradient at P as:

$$\nabla \phi = \frac{l\mathbf{s} + m\mathbf{t} + n\mathbf{u}}{2(A_1 + A_2 + A_3)} \tag{1}$$

We see that it is the sum of three vectors in the directions of $\mathbf{s}, \mathbf{t}$ and $\mathbf{u}$. Now the constant volume condition requires that we resolve the components of the gradient parallel to the plane ABC. To do this we will first look at the geometry represented by the various vectors above.

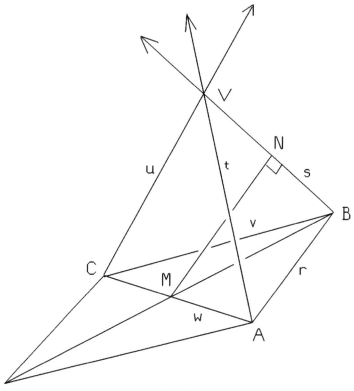

Fig. 71

To see the pure geometry, note that

$$\frac{l\mathbf{s}}{2} = \frac{\mathbf{s}.(\mathbf{r}-\mathbf{v})\mathbf{s}}{2\,s^2} = \frac{\hat{\mathbf{s}}.(\mathbf{r}-\mathbf{v})\hat{\mathbf{s}}}{2}$$

where $\hat{\mathbf{s}}$ is the unit vector in the direction of $\mathbf{s}$ and $(\mathbf{r}-\mathbf{v})$ is the diagonal of the parallelogram with $\mathbf{r}, \mathbf{v}$ as two defining edges, so $(\mathbf{r}-\mathbf{v})/2$ is the vector joining B to the mid-point M of AC. Hence

$$\frac{\hat{\mathbf{s}}.(\mathbf{r}-\mathbf{v})\hat{\mathbf{s}}}{2}$$

is the vector from B to the point N on BV where the line through M orthogonal to BV meets it. Similarly for $m\mathbf{t}/2$ and $n\mathbf{u}/2$. These are the three vectors which—when slid along $\mathbf{s}, \mathbf{t}, \mathbf{u}$ respectively to have their root points in V—sum to give the gradient (when divided by the areas term). Their resultant $\mathbf{g}$ does not in general pass through the circumcentre, as is seen by taking a small tetrahedron with $\mathbf{s}$ normal to ABC so that $l = 0$ and $\mathbf{g}$ lies in ACV, in which case ACV need not be a diametral plane of the circumsphere. This case also shows that $\mathbf{g}$ does not in general pass through the incentre either.

If ABC is equilateral and $s = t = u$ then $l = m = n$, and $l(\mathbf{s}+\mathbf{t}+\mathbf{u})$ is orthogonal to ABC and hence the strain component parallel to ABC is zero. If $s > r$ then there will be strain at the vertices A, B and C which means that the face ABC moves towards V, which remains stationary, until the tetrahedron becomes fully symmetrical, at which point there is no nett strain on the vertices.

If V is close to ABC and the tetrahedron is symmetrical otherwise, then ABC will move away from V, but also it will have to shrink to maintain the volume constant. Simulation shows this to be a very unstable and dynamic situation until full symmetry is attained. Thus in a liquid surface this situation will be widely prevalent, and if the base cannot move outwards due to other factors and yet needs to shrink we have a basis for surface tension.

If $\mathbf{h}$ is the unit height vector orthogonal to ABC pointing in the upward direction, and $\mathbf{g} = (l\mathbf{s}+m\mathbf{t}+n\mathbf{u})$, then the outer product $\mathbf{hXg}$ is a vector orthogonal to both, and the vector orthogonal to $\mathbf{hXg}$ and $\mathbf{h}$ is $(\mathbf{hXg})\,\mathbf{Xh}$, which is the component of $\mathbf{g}$ normal to $\mathbf{h}$ and hence parallel to ABC, and with the correct sense. The gradient $\nabla\phi$ in (1) may now be replaced by the constant volume gradient

$$\nabla\sigma = \frac{[\mathbf{hX}(l\mathbf{s}+m\mathbf{t}+n\mathbf{u})]\mathbf{Xh}}{2(A_1+A_2+A_3)}$$

where $\mathbf{h} = (\mathbf{rXv})/(rv.\sin(\mu))$ if μ is the angle between $\mathbf{r}$ and $\mathbf{v}$, i.e. $\mathbf{h} = (\mathbf{rXv})/(2A_4)$ where A_4 is the area of ABC, giving

$$\nabla\sigma = \frac{[(\mathbf{r}\mathbf{X}\mathbf{v})\mathbf{X}(l\mathbf{s} + m\mathbf{t} + n\mathbf{u})]\mathbf{X}(\mathbf{r}\mathbf{X}\mathbf{v})}{8\,A_4^2(A_1 + A_2 + A_3)} \tag{2}$$

We may reduce this to an expression that is more obviously parallel to ABC. Taking the first term of the numerator in [ ], we have

$$l(\mathbf{r}\mathbf{X}\mathbf{v})\mathbf{X}\mathbf{s} = l\mathbf{s}\mathbf{X}(\mathbf{v}\mathbf{X}\mathbf{r}) = l[(\mathbf{s}.\mathbf{r})\mathbf{v} - (\mathbf{s}.\mathbf{v})\mathbf{r}]$$

recalling that $\quad l = \dfrac{\mathbf{s}.(\mathbf{r} - \mathbf{v})}{s^2}$

we have for the first term

$$\frac{(\mathbf{s}.\mathbf{r} - \mathbf{s}.\mathbf{v})[(\mathbf{s}.\mathbf{r})\mathbf{v} - (\mathbf{s}.\mathbf{v})\mathbf{r}]}{s^2}$$

$$= (\hat{\mathbf{s}}.\mathbf{r} - \hat{\mathbf{s}}.\mathbf{v})[(\hat{\mathbf{s}}.\mathbf{r})\mathbf{v} - (\hat{\mathbf{s}}.\mathbf{v})\mathbf{r}]$$

$$= (\hat{\mathbf{s}}.\mathbf{r})^2\mathbf{v} + (\hat{\mathbf{s}}.\mathbf{v})^2\mathbf{r} - (\hat{\mathbf{s}}.\mathbf{r})(\hat{\mathbf{s}}.\mathbf{v})(\mathbf{r} + \mathbf{v})$$

$$= (\hat{\mathbf{s}}.\mathbf{r})^2\mathbf{v} + (\hat{\mathbf{s}}.\mathbf{v})^2\mathbf{r} + (\hat{\mathbf{s}}.\mathbf{r})(\hat{\mathbf{s}}.\mathbf{v})\mathbf{w}$$

Similarly for the second term using $\mathbf{w}\mathbf{X}\mathbf{r}$ instead of $\mathbf{r}\mathbf{X}\mathbf{v}$, since they are both $\mathbf{h}$ times the area of ABC, we get

$$(\hat{\mathbf{t}}.\mathbf{w})^2\mathbf{r} + (\hat{\mathbf{t}}.\mathbf{r})^2\mathbf{w} + (\hat{\mathbf{t}}.\mathbf{r})(\hat{\mathbf{t}}.\mathbf{w})\mathbf{v}$$

and for the third term, using $\mathbf{v}\mathbf{X}\mathbf{w}$, we get

$$(\hat{\mathbf{u}}.\mathbf{v})^2\mathbf{w} + (\hat{\mathbf{u}}.\mathbf{w})^2\mathbf{v} + (\hat{\mathbf{u}}.\mathbf{v})(\hat{\mathbf{u}}.\mathbf{w})\mathbf{r}$$

Combining these gives from (2)

$$\nabla\sigma = \frac{(\alpha\mathbf{r} + \beta\mathbf{v} + \gamma\mathbf{w})\mathbf{X}(\mathbf{r}\mathbf{X}\mathbf{v})}{8\,A_4^2(A_1 + A_2 + A_3)} \tag{3}$$

where

$$\alpha = (\hat{\mathbf{s}}.\mathbf{v})^2 + (\hat{\mathbf{t}}.\mathbf{w})^2 + (\hat{\mathbf{u}}.\mathbf{v})(\hat{\mathbf{u}}.\mathbf{w})$$

$$\beta = (\hat{\mathbf{s}}.\mathbf{r})^2 + (\hat{\mathbf{u}}.\mathbf{w})^2 + (\hat{\mathbf{t}}.\mathbf{r})(\hat{\mathbf{t}}.\mathbf{w})$$

$$\gamma = (\hat{\mathbf{t}}.\mathbf{r})^2 + (\hat{\mathbf{u}}.\mathbf{v})^2 + (\hat{\mathbf{s}}.\mathbf{r})(\hat{\mathbf{s}}.\mathbf{v})$$

Now, $\quad \mathbf{w}\mathbf{X}(\mathbf{r}\mathbf{X}\mathbf{v}) = (\mathbf{w}.\mathbf{v})\mathbf{r} - (\mathbf{w}.\mathbf{r})\mathbf{v}$

$\qquad\quad \mathbf{v}\mathbf{X}(\mathbf{w}\mathbf{X}\mathbf{r}) = (\mathbf{v}.\mathbf{r})\mathbf{w} - (\mathbf{v}.\mathbf{w})\mathbf{r} \quad$ using $\mathbf{w}\mathbf{X}\mathbf{r}$ in place of $\mathbf{r}\mathbf{X}\mathbf{v}$

$\qquad\quad \mathbf{r}\mathbf{X}(\mathbf{v}\mathbf{X}\mathbf{w}) = (\mathbf{r}.\mathbf{w})\mathbf{v} - (\mathbf{r}.\mathbf{v})\mathbf{w} \quad$ using $\mathbf{v}\mathbf{X}\mathbf{w}$ in place of $\mathbf{r}\mathbf{X}\mathbf{v}$

as $\mathbf{h} = (\mathbf{r}\mathbf{X}\mathbf{v})/2A_4 = (\mathbf{w}\mathbf{X}\mathbf{r})/2A_4 = (\mathbf{v}\mathbf{X}\mathbf{w})/2A_4$

Hence

$$\nabla\sigma = \frac{(\gamma - \beta)(\mathbf{v}.\mathbf{w})\mathbf{r} + (\alpha - \gamma)(\mathbf{r}.\mathbf{w})\mathbf{v} + (\beta - \alpha)(\mathbf{r}.\mathbf{v})\mathbf{w}}{8\,A_4^2(A_1 + A_2 + A_3)}$$

Since α, β, γ are scalars we see that this is a combination of $\mathbf{r}$, $\mathbf{v}$, $\mathbf{w}$ and hence clearly $\nabla\sigma$ is parallel to ABC as required. It might appear that the magnitudes s, t, u are not involved as α, β, γ involve $\hat{\mathbf{s}}$, $\hat{\mathbf{t}}$, $\hat{\mathbf{u}}$, but A_1, A_2, A_3 involve them.

$\nabla\sigma$ is zero if and only if $(\gamma - \beta)(\mathbf{v}.\mathbf{w}) = (\alpha - \gamma)\,(\mathbf{r}.\mathbf{w}) = (\beta - \alpha)\,(\mathbf{r}.\mathbf{v})$, for $\mathbf{r} + \mathbf{v} + \mathbf{w} = 0$. This is clearly satisfied if $\alpha = \beta = \gamma$, and is obviously satisfied for a symmetrical tetrahedron. It is clearer to see from (3) that $\alpha = \beta = \gamma$ is necessary as well as sufficient if the volume is not zero. If $r = v = w$ and $s = t = u$ then all the scalar products in α, β, γ are equal, so again $\nabla\sigma = 0$. The further away V is from ABC the smaller are the scalar products in α, β, γ and the larger are A_1, A_2, A_3, and hence the smaller is $\nabla\sigma$. Hence ABC will move towards V rather than the reverse.

For a given tetrahedron shape, the numerator is proportional to the fifth power of the scale while the denominator is proportional to its sixth power, so the stress on V is inversely proportional to the scale. Unlike molecular explanations this includes effects acting right across the liquid mass.

To calculate the direction of $\nabla\sigma$ we can use an alternative expansion of (3). Using the identity $\mathbf{a}\mathbf{X}(\mathbf{b}\mathbf{X}\mathbf{c}) = (\mathbf{a}.\mathbf{c})\mathbf{b} - (\mathbf{a}.\mathbf{b})\mathbf{c}$ we have

$$\nabla\sigma = (\alpha\mathbf{r}.\mathbf{v} + \beta\mathbf{v}^2 + \gamma\mathbf{v}.\mathbf{w})\mathbf{r} - (\alpha\mathbf{r}^2 + \beta\mathbf{r}.\mathbf{v} + \gamma\mathbf{r}.\mathbf{w})\mathbf{v} \qquad (4)$$

so that $\nabla\sigma$ is a combination of $\mathbf{r}$ and $\mathbf{v}$, and hence the direction is determined by the two scalars in brackets in the numerator. If they are k_r and k_v then the direction ψ wrt $\mathbf{r}$ in ABC is given by the cosine rule:

$$\cos\psi = \frac{(k_r r)^2 + g^2 - (k_v v)^2}{2(k_r r)g}$$

where $\mathbf{g} = (k_r\mathbf{r} - k_v\mathbf{v})$ is the numerator of (4) and is also the diagonal of the parallelogram with $k_r\mathbf{r}$ and $k_v\mathbf{v}$ as adjacent edges.

APPENDIX 6

PROLATE SPHEROID AS COUNTERSPACE SPHERE

We will now show that a prolate spheroid with a CSI at one focus and the zero-plane of the counterspace as the polar plane of that focus is a sphere in counterspace. We will show that the turns between that plane and all tangent planes are equal. Figure 72 below shows the spheroid with a focus at F where the CSI is located, and its polar plane ω through P. The various dimensions shown follow from the elementary theory of conic sections.

The semi-major and semi-minor axes are a and b respectively, and the third orthogonal to the page is also b.

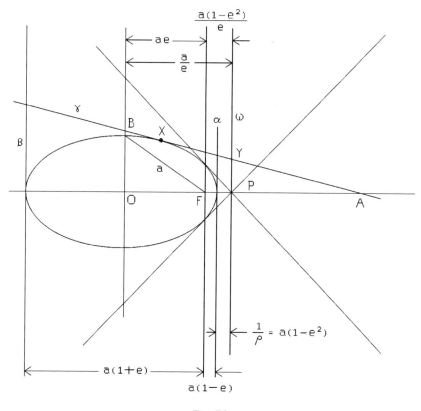

Fig. 72

The turn ρ between ω and the tangent plane α is

$$\frac{1}{a(1-e)} - \frac{e}{a(1-e^2)} = \frac{1}{a(1-e^2)}$$

and that between ω and β is

$$\frac{1}{a(1+e)} + \frac{e}{a(1-e^2)} = \frac{1}{a(1-e^2)}$$

so we see they are both the same. Note that the sign of the turns is important here.

Having shown the plausibility of the theorem, we must now establish it for the general case of a tangent plane g at a point $X = (x_1, 0, z_1, 1)$, which involves some algebra. This is eased if we first find the turn between ω and a general plane (orthogonal to the diagram, Fig. 73) through X and the point $Y = (x, 0, z, 1)$ on ω.

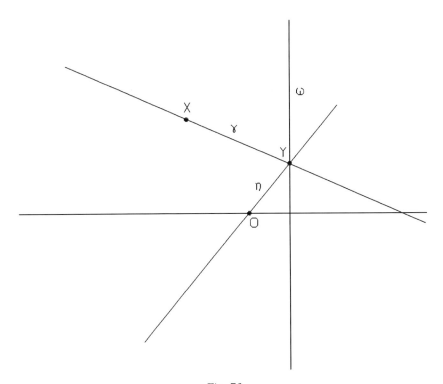

Fig. 73

The normalized co-ordinates of the plane η through Y and O are

$$\left(\frac{z}{\sqrt{x^2 + x^2}}, 0, \frac{-x}{\sqrt{x^2 + z^2}}, 0\right) \tag{1}$$

as is easily verified by taking the inner product of Y and η, and also noting that the y and w (fourth) co-ordinates are zero as η lies orthogonal to the page and passes through O. We have expressed this in normalized form ready to calculate turn as the parameter of the axial pencil in the line orthogonal to the page at Y (see Appendix 2).

The co-ordinates of w are

$$\left(\frac{-1}{x}, 0, 0, 1\right) \tag{2}$$

since it must contain the point $(x, 0, 0, 1)$ and is orthogonal to the page.

If the co-ordinates of the plane γ through X and Y are $(l, m, n, 1)$ then they must satisfy the inner product relationships

$$lx + nz + 1 = 0$$
$$lx_1 + nz_1 + 1 = 0$$

which we solve for l and n to give the plane

$$\left(\frac{z_1 - z}{x_1 z - x z_1}, 0, \frac{x - x_1}{x_1 z - x z_1}, 1\right) \tag{3}$$

Then the turn τ between w and γ is given by

$$\gamma = w + \tau \eta$$

and substituting the co-ordinates of the planes from (1) (2) and (3) gives

$$\left(\frac{z_1 - z}{x_1 z - x z_1}, 0, \frac{x - x_1}{x_1 z - x z_1}, 1\right) = \left(\frac{-1}{x} + \frac{\tau z}{\sqrt{x^2 + z^2}}, 0, \frac{-\tau x}{\sqrt{x^2 + z^2}}, 1\right)$$

Thus equating the ratios of the x and z co-ordinates on both sides and solving for τ we get

$$\tau = \frac{(x - x_1)\sqrt{x^2 + z^2}}{x(x z_1 - z x_1)} \tag{4}$$

For the general plane g shown tangential to the spheroid we must find $(x, 0, y, 1)$ for its intercept with w.

The equation of γ is

$$\frac{(x + ae)(x_1 + ae)}{a^2} + \frac{z z_1}{b^2} = 1$$

Now from the diagram it is clear that

$$x = \frac{a(1 - e^2)}{e} = \frac{b^2}{ae} \tag{5}$$

It is easiest to use simple proportion in the triangles OAB, PAY to find z. OB is given by substituting $x = -ae$ in the equation of γ to give

$$OB = \frac{b^2}{z_1}$$

The length of OA similarly follows from that equation with $z = 0$

$$OA = x + ae = \frac{a^2}{x_1 + ae}$$

Then PA $=$ OA $-$ OP $=$ OA $-$ a/e, and we finally get

$$PY = z = \frac{OB.PA}{OA} = \frac{-x_1 b^2}{z_1 ae} \tag{6}$$

Substituting for x and z from (5) and (6) in (4) and simplifying gives

$$\tau = \frac{\dfrac{b^2}{ae} - x_1}{\dfrac{b^2}{ae} \sqrt{z_1^2 + x_1^2}} \tag{7}$$

As a check, if we substitute $\{a(1-e), 0, 0, 1\}$ for X in the case of the tangent plane α we get $1/a(1 - e^2)$ as before.

Finally we must substitute for z_1 from the equation of the ellipse, which we will work out in detail as it requires some algebra.

From the equation of the conic we have

$$z_1^2 = b^2 \left(1 - \frac{(x_1 + ae)^2}{a^2} \right)$$

so for the inside of the square root of the denominator of (7) we get

$$x_1^2 + b^2 \left(1 - \frac{(x_1 + ae)^2}{a^2} \right) = x_1^2 + a^2(1 - e^2) - (x_1 + ae)^2(1 - e^2)$$

$$= a^2(1 - e^2) + e^2 x_1^2 - 2aex_1(1 - e^2) - a^2 e^2(1 - e^2)$$

$$= b^2(1 - e^2) + e^2 x_1^2 - 2bex_1 \sqrt{1 - e^2}$$

$$= \left(b\sqrt{1 - e^2} - ex_1 \right)^2$$

$$= e^2 \left(\frac{b^2}{ae} - x_1 \right)^2$$

Substituting this for $(x_1^2 + z_1^2)$ in (7) we get

$$\tau = \frac{a}{b^2} = \frac{1}{a(1 - e^2)} \tag{8}$$

that is, the turn between the tangent planes and ω is constant. Since the spheroid is symmetrical about the x-axis this shows that for counterspace the spatial prolate spheroid is a sphere with the above turn for its polar radius. This only applies, of course, if the CSI is at a focus.

Evidently for an oblate spheroid we do not get this, but for a CSI on its focal circle the vertical cross-sections are circular for counterspace, i.e. tangent cones to those cross-sections are circular.

A more elegant proof is given below for readers familiar with pedal curves and negative-pedal curves (Ref. 23).

Given a fixed line ω at a turn μ in from infinity (Fig. 74), and a variable

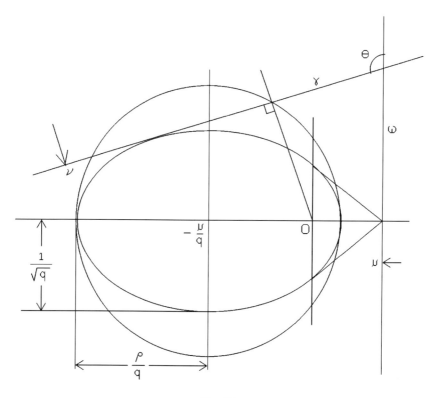

Fig. 74

line γ at a fixed turn ρ from this, we have using the cosine rule for the counterspace triangle $\omega\gamma\Omega$ (see Appendix 2)

$$\rho^2 = \nu^2 + \mu^2 - 2\nu\mu\cos(\theta)$$

where θ is the shift between the lines (γ, Ω) and (ω, Ω), which is the same as the angle between ω and γ, and ν is the turn of γ wrt Ω

so

$$\rho^2 = 1/r^2 + \mu^2 - 2\mu\cos(\theta/r) \quad \text{where } r = 1/\nu$$

i.e.

$$r^2(\rho^2 - \mu^2) = 1 - 2\mu r \cos(\theta)$$

If the line ω is vertical and the CSI is at O then $r.\cos(\theta) = x$, and we have

$$x^2 + y^2 + 2.x.\mu/q - 1/q = 0 \quad \text{where } q = \rho^2 - \mu^2$$

which is a circle centre $(-\mu/q, 0)$ and radius ρ/q. Thus the pedal points lie on a circle. The negative pedal of this is an ellipse, since the centre is not at the origin, with the horizontal major axis equal to the radius. The vertical (minor) axis b is given by $\theta = 90°$ and $270°$, i.e. $\nu = \sqrt{\rho^2 - \mu^2}$ so $b = 1/\sqrt{q}$. Thus as $a = \rho/q$, then from $b^2 = a^2(1 - e^2)$ the eccentricity is μ/ρ, and thus the CSI is at a focus since $a.e = \mu/q = $ the distance from the centre to a focus. The circle is thus the director circle of the ellipse. In other words the ellipse appears as a circle of radius ρ in counterspace with the CSI at a focus. Rotating the ellipse about its major axis thus gives a prolate spheroid which will appear as a sphere in counterspace as shown before.

Putting this another way:

when a sphere in counterspace does not have Ω as its centre it appears in space as a prolate spheroid.

As the ellipse gets bigger the eccentricity decreases, tending towards a circle when infinitely large. If $n = \mu$ we have $\rho = 0$ or $\rho = 2.\mu.\cos(\theta)$, i.e. $r.\cos(\theta) = x = 1/(2.\mu)$, so the pedal points lie on a vertical straight line giving a parabola for the pedal curve, as we expect for an eccentricity of 1.

Returning to the ellipse, the line γ has a shift of $180 - \theta$ wrt the other focus, which is an important fact for chemistry.

SPINORS

Generally a tensor in three dimensions may have one component and thus be a scalar, or three components in which case it is a vector, or more components for higher order tensors. But Eli Cartan (Ref. 7) discovered a linear representation of the three-dimensional orthogonal group (which leaves $g_{ij}x^i x^j$ invariant) with only two components, which he called a *spinor*. It is a representation which differs from the *faithful* or *true* representations such as vectors and bivectors since it involves an inescapable ambiguity in sign, as might be guessed from the fact that it has only two components.

Given an isotropic vector **x** for which $x_1^2 + x_2^2 + x_3^2 = 0$, the components of the associated spinor are defined as:

$$\xi_0 = \sqrt{\left(\frac{x_1 - ix_2}{2}\right)}$$

$$\xi_1 = \sqrt{\left(\frac{-x_1 - ix_2}{2}\right)} \tag{1}$$

for a three-dimensional Euclidean space. For counterspace the x_i represent turns.

The x_i may be expressed in terms of the spinor components as follows:

$$x_1 = \xi_0^2 - \xi_1^2$$
$$x_2 = i(\xi_0^2 + \xi_1^2) \tag{2}$$
$$x_3 = -2\xi_0\xi_1$$

The matrices representing the group are the Pauli spin matrices:

$$H_1 = \begin{pmatrix} 0 & 1 \\ 1 & 0 \end{pmatrix}, \quad H_2 = \begin{pmatrix} 0 & -i \\ i & 0 \end{pmatrix}, \quad H_3 = \begin{pmatrix} 1 & 0 \\ 0 & -1 \end{pmatrix}$$

for which

$$H_i^2 = 1, H_i H_j + H_j H_i = 0$$

For ordinary vectors we have a basis in terms of which others are expressed, e.g. $\hat{\mathbf{i}}, \hat{\mathbf{j}}, \hat{\mathbf{k}}$ representing the basic unit vectors for orthogonal Euclidean space, so that a vector (x_1, x_2, x_3) is also expressed as $x_1\hat{\mathbf{i}} + x_2\hat{\mathbf{j}} + x_3\hat{\mathbf{k}}$. For the spin group the *Hi* play the same role as the basic unit vectors, so that a member of that group is $x_1H_1 + x_2H_2 + x_3H_3$, i.e.

$$\begin{bmatrix} x_3 & x_1 - ix_2 \\ x_1 + ix_2 & -x_3 \end{bmatrix}$$

Although these transformations are rotation-like, in that they involve no translation and if **x** is a unit vector then no expansion either, they are not in general simple rotations, except the vector $(0, i, 0)$ which gives the matrix

$$\begin{bmatrix} 0 & 1 \\ -1 & 0 \end{bmatrix}$$

which can be interpreted as a rotation through $90°$.

The general representation for any number of dimensions satisfies the same conditions, usually denoted by E_i to distinguish it from the Pauli matrices. Thus a group member is represented by

$$X_i = x_1E_1 + x_2E_2 + \ldots$$

so that

$$X^2 = \Sigma x_i^2 E_i^2 + \Sigma x_i x_j \left(E_i E_j + E_j E_i\right)$$
$$= \Sigma(x_i^2 I) \quad \text{where I} = \text{unit matrix}$$

and we see that X^2 is invariant as required for a Euclidean representation of the orthogonal group.

The isotropic vector associated with a spinor can be regarded as a ruler of the imaginary cone represented by **v**, with parameter ξ_0/ξ_1 (*op. cit.*). This is based on the following equations for the two planes that intersect in the generator of the cone:

$$\xi_0 x_3 + \xi_1(x_1 - ix_2) = 0$$
$$\xi_0(x_1 + ix_2) - \xi_1 x_3 = 0$$

where the ξ_i constitute the homogeneous parameter, and $x_4 = 0$ as the planes lie in the vertex at the origin. Purely projectively it is only the *ratio* ξ_0/ξ_1 that is significant, but the spinor relates to their absolute (complex) values. Thus there are orthogonal transformations (the spin transformations) that not only leave the parameter ξ_0/ξ_1 invariant but also the values of the ξ_i individually. If we rotate **v** round the surface of the cone then ξ_0/ξ_1 comes back to its original value after one complete rotation, but the ξ_i end up with opposite sign. So we see that for a real cone there would be ∞^1 values of ξ_0 (and also ξ_1) for a given generator, and for a complex one

∞^2. The equations for the ξ_i given above select just one spinor from these, independently of x_3 which is then defined as $-2\xi_0\xi_1$. It seems that only one particular constitution of the parameter is invariant as a spinor.

We may interpret the idea of an isotropic vector in an interesting way. The projective equation $x_0^2 + x_1^2 + x_2^2 = 0 = x_3$ is the equation of the Euclidean absolute circle at infinity, i.e. of the metric quadric of space. In counterspace co-ordinates it is that of the absolute cone. Thus a particular isotropic vector can be seen as representing a point on the absolute circle and a tangent plane of the absolute cone. A homography is implied if we see this as a linkage between space and counterspace as the same formal co-ordinates represent both the absolute circle in space and the absolute cone in counterspace, and hence a correspondence between their points and planes. The tangent plane contains both a generator of the cone and a tangent of the circle. According to Cartan's interpretation of $\lambda = \xi_0/\xi_1$ of a spinor, λ is the parameter of these two lines.

Summarizing,

1. We are concerned with isotropic vectors representing points and planes of the absolutes.
2. The parameter $\lambda = \xi_0/\xi_1$ relates corresponding generators, and the associated spinors are the particular valid values of (ξ_0, ξ_1) which correspond to each λ.
3. There is an orthogonal linear transformation (both absolutes invariant) for which these spinors are tensors.

It is now clear that given the isotropic vector and implied homography there is a linear orthogonal transformation for which all these associated spinors are tensors.

The situation is complicated by an important fact: spinors are metric entities and have no analogue in affine geometry. In a sense this is obvious as the metric quadrics are essentially involved.

Of particular interest is the fact that the outer product of *pairs* of spinors has a tensorial character as it leaves both a trivector (polar volume) and a vector invariant (*op. cit.*, page 48) so that associated with that outer product (of degree 4) we have the vector

$$
\begin{bmatrix}
\xi_0' \, \xi_0 - \xi_1' \, \xi_1 \\
i(\xi_0' \, \xi_0 + \xi_1' \, \xi_1) \\
-\xi_0' \, \xi_1 - \xi_1' \, \xi_0
\end{bmatrix}
$$

and the trivector with volume $(\xi_0' \, \xi_1 - \xi_1' \, \xi_0)$.

Thus if we have a spinor associated with each of two CSIs then there is a vector **s** and a trivector **V** associated with them, which are tensors. The trivector relates to volume or polar volume. If ξ and ξ' are the same then from (2) and (3) above the vector is simply that of the spinors themselves. However in this case it also follows from (3) that the polar volume involved is zero, even if the signs of the components of ξ and ξ' are opposite.

Cartan also shows (*op. cit.*, page 50) that for real Euclidean space the product of a spinor and the conjugate of another spinor yields a scalar together with a bivector. The conjugate of a spinor is $iC\bar{\xi}$ given by

$$iC\bar{\xi} = i\begin{bmatrix} 0 & 1 \\ -1 & 0 \end{bmatrix}\bar{\xi}$$
$$= \begin{bmatrix} 0 & 1 \\ -1 & 0 \end{bmatrix}\begin{bmatrix} \xi_1 \\ \xi_0 \end{bmatrix}$$
$$= \begin{bmatrix} \xi_0 \\ -\xi_1 \end{bmatrix}$$

Thus we see that the conjugate spinors are also tensors of significance related to the ordinary ones. We cannot totally identify them, however, as a conjugate spinor is of a different type from the normal ones, as its behaviour wrt reflection differs. We may take a spinor together with its conjugate and form the product, which is then a tensor giving (*op. cit.*) a scalar

$$\xi_0\bar{\xi}_0 + \xi_1\bar{\xi}_1 = \sqrt{x_1^2 + x_2^2}$$

and a bivector

$$\begin{bmatrix} \xi_0\bar{\xi}_1 + \xi_1\bar{\xi}_0 \\ i(\xi_0\bar{\xi} - \xi_1\bar{\xi}_0) \\ \xi_0\bar{\xi}_0 - \xi_1\bar{\xi}_1 \end{bmatrix} = \begin{bmatrix} \dfrac{\sqrt{x_2^2 - x_1^2 + i2x_1x_2} + \sqrt{x_2^2 - x_1^2 - i2x_1x_2}}{2} \\ \dfrac{\sqrt{x_2^2 - x_1^2 - i2x_1x_2} - \sqrt{x_2^2 - x_1^2 + i2x_1x_2}}{2} \\ 0 \end{bmatrix} = \begin{bmatrix} x_2 \\ -x_1 \\ 0 \end{bmatrix}$$

If $x_1 = ix_2$ then the scalar is zero and we have an isotropic bivector. The bivector is real if both x_1 and x_2 are real in which case $-x_3^2 = x_1^2 + x_2^2$. The scalar is then also real. The bivector determines its orientation, which is fixed for a given linkage as the third co-ordinate is zero.

We are interested in these facts about spinors for further development of the work where we need to relate light represented by bivectors and chemical action in relation to trivectors.

APPENDIX 8

PATH CURVES

Path curves were first discovered by Felix Klein, and arise when a linear transformation is applied repeatedly. George Adams found that for special cases egg forms and vortices arise. For a description of path curves the reader is referred to the work of Edwards in Ref. 11, so that for the sake of brevity we may use matrix methods in this appendix. A linear projective transformation in three dimensions is characterized by

$$\mathbf{x}' = \mathbf{A}\mathbf{x}$$

where $\mathbf{A}$ is the 4×4 transformation matrix consisting of constants, $\mathbf{x}$ is a vector representing a point in homogeneous co-ordinates and $\mathbf{x}'$ is its transform. We may now repeat the transform for $\mathbf{x}'$:

$$\mathbf{x}'' = \mathbf{A}\mathbf{x}'$$

and repeat this to give a series of points $\mathbf{x}$, $\mathbf{x}'$, $\mathbf{x}''$ ... which lie on a curve called a path curve. The curve is one of a whole family of invariant curves for the transform which cover the whole of space so that every point in space lies on one such curve.

Dually $\mathbf{x}$ may be the co-ordinates of a plane in which case we obtain a series of planes which form a *developable*, which is a single parameter family of planes dual to a curve. The developable has a *cuspidal edge* that coincides with a path curve. A surface arises formed of the tangents to the cuspidal edge, and if it is cut along this edge the resulting sheets of the surface may be laid out flat, as the surface has zero curvature.

The eigenvectors of the matrix $\mathbf{A}$ give four points which are self-corresponding determining an invariant tetrahedron, and the dual inter-pretation of those vectors gives four planes which are the faces of that tetrahedron. Edwards has mainly worked with a particular tetrahedron which has two real parallel planes, two imaginary planes, two real edges one of which (the axis) is orthogonal to the real planes and the other polar to it lying in Ω, and four imaginary edges (Fig. 75).

In this case $\mathbf{A}$ has two complex conjugate eigenvalues and two real ones, and the path curves for such transformations either lie on egg-shaped or vortex-shaped surfaces which may have circular symmetry about the axis, or may have horizontal cross-sections which are logarithmic spirals. A typical tetrahedron and path curve is shown in Fig. 76.

In Chapter 16 we considered a correlation from space to counterspace

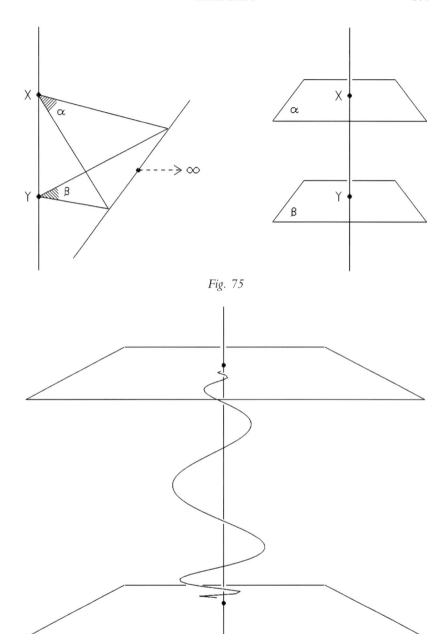

Fig. 75

Fig. 76

composed of a polarity and a rotation. The self-polar surface was a spheroid. A general correlation is the sum of a symmetrical matrix $\mathbf{S}$ and a skew-symmetric null polarity $\mathbf{N}$ (e.g. Ref. 19), where $\mathbf{S}$ represents the self-polar quadric and $\mathbf{N}$ the rotation, so the correlation for our spheroid will be $\mathbf{S}+\mathbf{N}$. For the reverse transformation from counterspace to space the spheroid appears to be of opposite type to $\mathbf{S}$, e.g. if $\mathbf{S}$ is prolate then in counterspace it is oblate. Denote this by $\mathbf{S}^*$. Thus if we start with a point $\mathbf{x}$ in space the first transformation will give the plane $\mathbf{u}$ as follows

$$\mathbf{u} = (\mathbf{S}+\mathbf{N})\mathbf{x}$$

while the second will transform $\mathbf{u}$ back to a point again

$$\mathbf{x}' = (\mathbf{S}^* + \mathbf{N}^{-1})\mathbf{u}$$

noting that we use the inverse of $\mathbf{N}$ for the reverse transformation, so the total transformation is

$$\mathbf{x}'(\mathbf{S}^* + \mathbf{N}^{-1})\,(\mathbf{S}+\mathbf{N})\mathbf{x} \tag{1}$$

If the spheroid $\mathbf{S}$ has the equation

$$\frac{x^2}{a^2} + \frac{y^2}{b^2} + \frac{z^2}{b^2} = 1$$

then the matrix $\mathbf{S}$ is

$$\begin{bmatrix} \dfrac{1}{a^2} & & & \\ & \dfrac{1}{b^2} & & \\ & & \dfrac{1}{b^2} & \\ & & & -1 \end{bmatrix}$$

In counterspace the equation of the spheroid is

$$a^2\xi^2 + b^2\eta^2 + b^2\zeta^2 = 1$$

where (ξ, η, ζ) are the counterspace turn co-ordinates, so we see that $\mathbf{S}^* = \mathbf{S}^{-1}$. Thus (1) becomes

$$\mathbf{x}' = (\mathbf{S}^{-1} + \mathbf{N}^{-1})\,(\mathbf{S}+\mathbf{N})\mathbf{x}$$
$$= (2\mathbf{I} + \mathbf{N}^{-1}\mathbf{S} + \mathbf{S}^{-1}\mathbf{N})\mathbf{x}$$
$$= \mathbf{A}\mathbf{x}$$

Consider now the eigenvalues of $\mathbf{A}$. To find them we must solve

$$(2\mathbf{I} + \mathbf{N}^{-1}\mathbf{S} + \mathbf{S}^{-1}\mathbf{N}) \mathbf{x} = \lambda \mathbf{x}$$

i.e.

$$(\mathbf{N}^{-1}\mathbf{S} + \mathbf{S}^{-1}\mathbf{N}) \mathbf{x} = (\lambda - 2)\mathbf{x} \tag{2}$$

Now the eigenvalues of $\mathbf{N}^{-1}\mathbf{S}$ are given by

$$\mathbf{N}^{-1}\mathbf{S}\mathbf{y} = \mu\mathbf{y}$$

and multiplying both sides by $\mathbf{S}^{-1}\mathbf{N}$ we have

$$\mathbf{y} = \mu\mathbf{S}^{-1}\mathbf{N}\mathbf{y}$$

which is the eigenvalue equation for $\mathbf{S}^{-1}\mathbf{N}$, so that $\mathbf{N}^{-1}\mathbf{S}$ and $\mathbf{S}^{-1}\mathbf{N}$ have reciprocal eigenvalues. Thus it follows that they have the same types of eigenvalues (i.e. each either real or imaginary), and since from (2)

$$\lambda - 2 = \mu + 1/\mu$$

then $\mathbf{A}$ has the same types also. Regarded as a pointwise transformation $\mathbf{S}^{-1}$ is an expansion which leaves Ω invariant, $\mathbf{N}$ necessarily leaves Ω invariant, and also the axis of rotation of $\mathbf{N}$ is left invariant by $\mathbf{S}^{-1}$, so that the product of $\mathbf{S}^{-1}$ and $\mathbf{N}$ leaves that axis and Ω invariant. It follows that $\mathbf{S}^{-1}\mathbf{N}$ has two real and two complex conjugate eigenvalues to give the resulting rotation and expansion (Ref. 27 describes the relationship of eigenvalues to transformations). Then $\mathbf{A}$ has the same types of eigenvalues and thus gives a path curve transformation with a semi-imaginary tetrahedron of the type employed by Edwards in the study of buds and vortices.

The above approach saves reproducing lengthy explicit matrix manipulations, which the sceptical reader is cordially invited to carry out. It should be noted that a null polarity $\mathbf{N}$ may have an inverse if it is 4×4, but is singular if 3×3. The essence of assuming the quadric is of different type in the two spaces lies in taking the transformation from counterspace back to space as $\mathbf{S}^{-1} + \mathbf{N}^{-1}$ instead of $(\mathbf{S} + \mathbf{N})^{-1}$; the latter would merely give an identity instead of path curves.

REFERENCES

1. *Space and the Light of Creation*, George Adams Kaufmann, published by the Author, London 1933.
2. *The Lemniscatory Ruled Surface in Space and Counterspace*, George Adams, Rudolf Steiner Press, London 1979.
3. *Universal Forces in Mechanics*, George Adams, Rudolf Steiner Press, London 1977.
4. *The Plant Between Sun and Earth*, George Adams and Olive Whicher, Rudolf Steiner Press, London 1980.
5. *Molecular Quantum Mechanics*, P.W. Atkins, Oxford University Press, 1983.
6. *Wholeness and the Implicate Order*, David Bohm, Routledge & Kegan Paul, London 1980.
7. *The Theory of Spinors*, Élie Cartan, Dover, 1966.
8. *Introduction to Geometry*, H.S.M. Coxeter, John Wiley & Sons, London 1969.
9. *Elements of Projective Geometry*, Luigi Cremona, Dover Publications, New York 1960.
10. *Projective Geometry*, Lawrence Edwards, Rudolf Steiner Institute, Phoenixville 1985.
11. *The Vortex of Life*, Lawrence Edwards, Floris Books, Edinburgh 1993.
12. *Projective Geometry*, T. Ewan Faulkner, Oliver & Boyd, London 1960.
13. *An Introduction to Quantum Physics*, A.P. French and E.F. Taylor, Van Nostrand Reinhold (UK), Wokingham 1978.
14. *Partial Differentiation*, R.P. Gillespie, Oliver & Boyd, London 1951.
15. *Chaos*, James Gleick, Sphere Books, London 1987.
16. 'Tip and Whorl Morphogenesis in *Acetabularia* by Calcium-regulated Strain Fields', B.C. Goodwin and L.E.H. Trainor, in *Journal of Theoretical Biology* (1985), 117, 79–106, Academic Press (London).
17. *Raum, Zeit, Geschwindigkeit*, Peter Geschwind, Mathematisch-Astronomische Sektion Goetheanum, Dornach 1986.
18. *Philosophical Problems of Quantum Physics*, Werner Heisenberg, Ox Bow Press, Woodbridge, Connecticut 1979.
19. *A Treatise on the Line Complex*, C.M. Jessop, Cambridge University Press, Cambridge 1903.
20. 'The Turning Point', Ralph Kronig, in *Theoretical Physics in the Twentieth Century: A Memorial Volume to Wolfgang Pauli*, edited by Fierz and Weisskopf, New York 1960.
21. *An Introduction to Tensor Calculus, Relativity and Cosmology*, D.F. Lawden, Wiley, London 1986.
22. *Raum und Gegenraum*, Louis Locher-Ernst, Philosophisch-Anthroposophischer Verlag am Goetheanum, Dornach 1957.
23. *A Book of Curves*, E.H. Lockwood, Cambridge University Press, Cambridge 1978.

24. *Introduction to Quantum Mechanics with Applications to Chemistry*, Linus Pauling and E. Bright Wilson Jr., Dover Publications, New York 1985.

25. *Shadows of the Mind*, Roger Penrose, Oxford University Press, Oxford 1994.

26. 'Autobiographical Note' in *Albert Einstein: Philosopher-Scientist*, edited by P.A. Schlipp, Evanston, Ill. 1949.

27. *Algebraic Projective Geometry*, Semple and Kneebone, Oxford University Press, Oxford 1952.

28. *Special Functions of Mathematical Physics and Chemistry*, Ian N. Sneddon, Oliver & Boyd, London 1956.

29. *Tensor Calculus*, Barry Spain, Oliver & Boyd, London 1953.

30. *The Philosophy of Spiritual Activity*, Rudolf Steiner, Rudolf Steiner Press, London 1979.

31. *The Inner Experience of Music*, Rudolf Steiner, 26 November 1906 (GA 283).

32. *The Evolution of Consciousness*, Rudolf Steiner, August 1923, Penmaenmawr (GA 227).

33. *The Etherization of the Blood*, Rudolf Steiner, 1 October 1912, Basle.

34. *Man as Symphony of the Creative Word*, Rudolf Steiner, November 1923, Dornach (GA 230).

35. *Heat Course*, Rudolf Steiner, March 1920, Stuttgart (GA 321).

36. *Light Course*, Rudolf Steiner, December/January 1919/20, Stuttgart (GA 320).

37. *Man Heiroglyph of the Universe*, Rudolf Steiner, May 1920, Dornach (GA 201).

38. *Analytic and Projective Geometry*, Dirk J. Struik, Addison-Wesley Publishing Co., London 1953.

39. *Projective and Analytical Geometry*, J.A. Todd, Pitman, London 1947.

40. *Projective Geometry*, Veblen and Young, Ginn and Company, Boston 1910.

41. 'Thermal Expansion in Counterspace', P.P. Veugelers, Articles Supplement of the *Newsletter* of the Science Group of the Anthroposophical Society in Great Britain, September 1997.

42. *Projective Geometry*, Olive Whicher, Rudolf Steiner Press, London 1971.

43. *Catching the Light*, Arthur Zajonc, Transworld Publishers, London 1993.

44. 'Ein neues Resultat zum Thema fünfte Kraft', B. Hubler, A. Cornaz, W. Kündig, *Phys.Bl.* 50 (1994), Nr. 9, Weinheim 1994.

45. *A New Science of Life*, Rupert Sheldrake, Blond & Briggs, London 1981.

INDEX

absolute circle at infinity, 17, 18, 125, 141, 143, 148, 176

absolute cone at infinity, 18, 42, 125, 141, 148, 176

Adams, George, 1–2, 10, 12, 18–19, 42, 46, 52, 72–3, 178

affine fluidity, 65, 80, 81

affine geometry, 14–18, 60, 61–2, 84, 85, 108, 117, 151

affine state, 63, 117
  transition to metric, 63, 65, 130

Aspect, Alain, 84, 93

atoms, atomic theory, 63, 65, 81, 105, 106, 116, 122–3, 129ff.
  orbitals, 116, 129, 131, 132

Avogadro's constant, 65

Balmer series, 99

Bell's Inequality, 93, 133

bivectors, 84–6, 88–90, 174, 177
  representing photon cylinder, 130

black holes, 56, 106

Bohm, David, 2, 122, 135, 136

Bohr, Niels, 131

Bohr radius, 126

bonding, see chemistry

Born, Max, 131, 132

Bose-Einstein statistics, 132

bosons, 132

Boyle's Law, 65, 72

Brianchon, Charles Julien, 8–9

Brianchon's Theorem, 8–9

Brownian motion, 71

Cartan, Élie, 125, 174, 176–7

Cayley, Arthur, 16, 18, 62
  formula, 16, 144

centro-affine geometry, 15

chaos game, 46, 127

chemical (tone, number) ether, 61–2, 96, 97, 105, 115, 131, 132, 134

chemistry, 61–2, 134, 177
  bonding, 103, 104, 117, 118, 123

elements, 122–3

chord law, 49, 52, 56, 59, 63, 64, 67, 157–61

coefficient of expansion, 79

Collage Theorem, 46–7

collineations, 5, 13

colour, 97, 100

Compton scatter, 89

cones, 4–5, 85, 175
  affinely linked, 134
  imaginary, 18, 52, 175
  polar area of, 28–31, 41, 85–6, 90–91, 94ff., 123
  See also photon cones

conics, conic sections, 8–9, 10, 117, 168

consciousness, states of, 14, 19, 133, 135

contravariance 58, 72, 73, 84–8, 139

correlations, 5, 13

cosine rule for counterspace, 21, 53, 144–6, 173

Coulomb force, 44, 137

counterspace, 1, 12ff., 18–22, 42ff., 134
  distinguished from polar-Euclidean space, 42
  infinities (CSIs), 3, 42–3, 46ff.
  primal, 47, 78, 81, 107, 116, 122, 123, 132, 133
  relating to living organisms, 119–21, 125–8
  relating to the ethers, 108, 133
  time structure for, 106

covariance, 72–3, 84–8, 139

cross-ratio, 5–6, 12, 14, 16, 17, 18, 46

crystals, 52, 60, 71, 106, 128

cube linked to counterspace, 42–3, 45

curvature, 18, 28ff.

de Broglie wave, 84

density, 52, 54, 55, 56

division ratios, 14–15, 84

duality principle, 8–9, 19, 20, 28, 141
  See also polar area, polar volume

Edwards, Lawrence, 181